13+ Science

For the Common Entrance exams

The best way to get to grips with 13+ Science is to do stacks of practice questions. Luckily for you, this fantastic CGP book is bursting with them!

There are questions for every topic, covering everything from combustion and photosynthesis to the Solar System. We've even included questions on the practicals.

You'll find practice papers and detailed answers for every question at the back of the book, so you'll be in tip-top exam shape in no time. There's also an extra Foundation Level paper in the Online Edition!

How to access your free Online Edition

This book includes a free Online Edition to read on your PC, Mac or tablet. You'll just need to go to **cgpbooks.co.uk/extras** and enter this code:

1622 5594 4515 1903

By the way, this code only works for one person. If somebody else has used this book before you, they might have already claimed the Online Edition.

Exam Practice Workbook

Published by CGP

From original material by Paddy Gannon.

Editors:
Ellen Burton, Katie Fernandez, Luke Molloy, Georgina Paxman,
Rachael Rogers, Camilla Sheridan and Tamara Sinivassen

With thanks to Barrie Crowther for the proofreading.

With thanks to Jan Greenway for the copyright research.

ISBN: 978 1 78908 794 9
Printed by Elanders Ltd, Newcastle upon Tyne.
Clipart from Corel®
Illustrations by: Sandy Gardner Artist, email sandy@sandygardner.co.uk

Contents

Section C1 — States of Matter

Section C2 — Atoms, Elements, Molecules and Compounds

Section C3 — Purity, Mixtures and Separating Mixtures

Section C4 — Combustion and Thermal Decomposition

Section C5 — Oxidation Reactions, Acids and Alkalis

Section P1 — Energy Transfers and Resources

Section P2 — Speed and Forces

Section P3 — Pressure and Density

Section P4 — Sound and Light

Section P5 — Circuits and Magnets

Section P6 — Space

Practice Papers

All of these practice papers, plus an additional Foundation practice paper, are available online (see p.2).

How to Use This Book

Have a look at the following information — it might just come in handy...

There are **Two Levels** in **Common Entrance 13+ Science**

1) You can either do **Foundation Level** or **Level 2** exams for **Common Entrance 13+ Science** (the Level 2 exams are a bit **harder)**.

2) You'll do **one paper** for the **Foundation Level** exam, and it tests you on all three science subjects (Biology, Chemistry and Physics).

3) You'll do **three separate papers** for the **Level 2** exams — one for each of the three sciences.

You're allowed to take a calculator and a protractor into all exams with you.

This Book Has Some **Useful Features**

This book is split up into **16 sections**. Each section is split into different **topics**, so you can practise the bits you need.

No matter what exam you do, at least **25%** of each paper will test your **Thinking and Working as a Scientist** skills. Practical based questions that really test these skills have been marked up with a **stamp** like this.

31

Investigating Populations   PRACTICAL

Q1 A student wants to investigate the number of woodlice in her garden.

(a) (i) Name a technique the student could use to capture woodlice for counting.

.... (1)

(ii) Describe how the technique given in (i) can be used to count woodlice.

....

....

.... (2)

(b) Suggest one way that the student could make sure her investigation produces reliable results.

.... (1)

Q2 A student is estimating the number of buttercups in his garden.

He uses the piece of equipment shown on the right.

(a) Name this piece of equipment.

.... (1)

The student places this piece of equipment at five random sample points in his garden. He counts the number of buttercups inside the frame at each point. His results are shown in this table.

Sample point	1	2	3	4	5
Number of buttercups	12	8	9	4	7

(b) Calculate the mean number of buttercups.

No. of buttercups = ... (2)

(c) The student works out that his garden has an area of 32 m². The frame he used had an area of 1 m². Calculate an estimate of the size of the population of buttercups in the garden.

Population size = ... (1)

/ 8

☹ ✓   😐 ✓   🙂 ✓   Section B4 — Interdependence and Populations

---

Use this space to write your **answer**. The number tells you how many **marks** this question or question part is worth.

For calculation questions, there's space to do your **working**.

Use the **detailed answers** (p.152) to mark your work. Write your **score** in the box at the end of each topic.

Tick the box that matches how confident you feel with the **questions** in each topic. This should help show you where you need to **focus** your **revision**.

There is also a full set of **Level 2 practice papers** at the end of this book, and a **Foundation Level practice paper** in your **Online Edition**. You can download any of these papers by going to **cgpbooks.co.uk/extras** and entering the code at the front of this book.

Cells

Q1 The diagram below shows a typical plant cell.

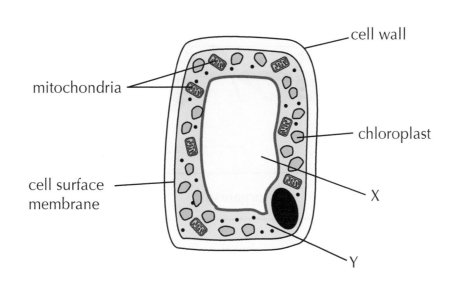

(a) State the functions of the following parts of the cell.

cell wall: ....

....

cell surface membrane: ....

....

mitochondria: ....

....

chloroplast: ....

.... (4)

(b) State the name of structure X.

.... (1)

(c) (i) State the name of the feature labelled Y.

.... (1)

(ii) State the function of feature Y.

.... (1)

/ 7

More on Cells

Q1 The diagram below shows the levels of organisation in a plant.

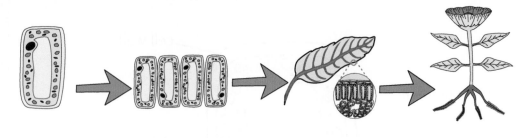

....

| organ | tissue | organism | cell |

(a) Use the words from the box above to label the diagram.

(1)

(b) The root system is an example of an organ system in plants.
Describe what an organ system is.

....

.... (1)

Q2 There are seven life processes carried out by all organisms.

(a) In humans, there is a tube through which urine (a liquid containing waste products) exits the body. This tube is called the urethra.
State which one of the seven life processes this function of the urethra carries out.

.... (1)

(b) Human skin tissue has nerves. When a person touches an object, nerves allow them to feel the object's texture and temperature.
State which one of the seven life processes this function of the nerves carries out.

.... (1)

(c) Name two other life processes that have not already been stated.

1. ....

2. .... (1)

/ 5

The Light Microscope PRACTICAL

Q1 Anita is preparing a microscope slide of some onion cells using water.

(a) Describe the steps Anita should take to prepare the slide.

....

....

....

....

.... (3)

eyepiece lens

rough focusing knob

objective lens

stage

fine focusing knob

mirror

(b) Anita places the slide on the stage of a microscope.
She angles the mirror so that light shines up through the hole in the stage.
Give one safety precaution she should take when changing the mirror angle.

....

.... (1)

(c) Anita selects a suitable objective lens.
Describe how Anita could focus the microscope on the onion cells.

....

....

....

.... (2)

(d) Name a stain that Anita could add to the slide to see the cells more clearly.

.... (1)

(e) Anita is using an eyepiece lens with a magnification of × 100 and an objective lens with a magnification of × 10.
Calculate the total magnification of the image that Anita is viewing.

Total magnification = × .... (1)

Q2 Jonah is using a light microscope to view a leaf from Elodea, which is a type of plant that grows in water.

(a) The real width of the leaf is 3 mm. Jonah is viewing it at a magnification of × 40.
Calculate the width of the image of the leaf at this magnification.

Use the formula: magnification = $\dfrac{\text{image size}}{\text{real size}}$

Show your working.

Image width = ... mm (2)

Jonah increases the magnification to view an individual cell.
He draws a diagram showing the cell. It is shown below.

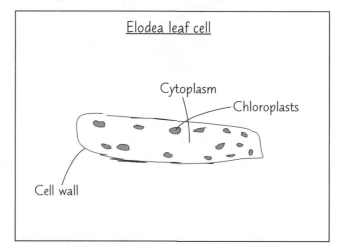

(b) Give three ways that Jonah could improve his diagram.

1. ....

....

2. ....

....

3. ....

.... (3)

/ 13

Nutrition

Q1 A balanced human diet contains many different nutrients.
Underline the function of each of the following nutrients.

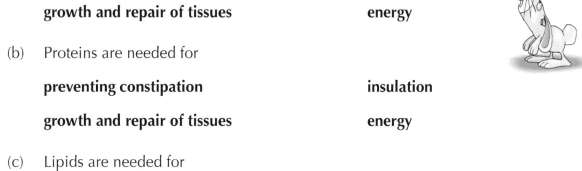

    (a)   Carbohydrates are needed for

        preventing constipation   **insulation**

        growth and repair of tissues   **energy**

        (1)

    (b)   Proteins are needed for

        preventing constipation   **insulation**

        growth and repair of tissues   **energy**

        (1)

    (c)   Lipids are needed for

        preventing constipation   **repair of tissues**

        growth   **energy and insulation**

        (1)

Q2 There are seven important components of a healthy human diet.

    (a)   Complete the table below to show which component of a healthy diet each food is a good source of. Use each component once.

Food Source	Component
Oranges	Vitamins
Butter	
Fish	
Cup of coffee	
Potatoes	
Table salt	
Carrots	

        (6)

    (b)   Explain why water is an important part of the diet.

....

....   (1)

/ 10

Staying Healthy

Q1 An unbalanced diet can lead to health problems.

(a) (i) Underline the word which correctly completes the following sentence.

Calcium salts are an example of a

lipid   **protein**   **vitamin**   **mineral**

(1)

(ii) Describe one effect a lack of calcium can have on human health.

....

(1)

(b) State the deficiency disease caused by a lack of vitamin C.

....

(1)

Q2 Health problems can be caused by eating too much or too little food.

(a) Explain what can happen if a person doesn't eat enough food.

....

....

....

(2)

(b) Eating too much food can cause obesity.
(i) State two health problems that obesity can lead to.

1. ....

2. ....

(2)

The food labels for two ready meals are shown below.

Meal A:

Nutrient	Energy	Fat	Saturates	Carbohydrate	Sugars	Fibre	Protein	Salt
per 100 g	360 kcal	2.4 g	0.8 g	11.1 g	2.5 g	4.5 g	4.3 g	0.6 g

Meal B:

Nutrient	Energy	Fat	Saturates	Carbohydrate	Sugars	Fibre	Protein	Salt
per 100 g	140 kcal	2.4 g	0.2 g	18 g	1 g	4.5 g	4.9 g	0.31 g

(ii) State which meal a person trying to limit their intake of saturated fat should have.

....

(1)

(iii) Explain the potential effect on the body of eating too much saturated fat.

....

....

(1)

/ 9

Food Tests

Q1 Alyssa wants to carry out tests on some bread to find out which nutrients it contains.

To prepare some samples of the bread for testing, Alyssa first takes a small piece and grinds it up using a pestle and mortar.

(a) Describe what else she should do to prepare the food sample before testing.

....

....

....

.... (3)

Alyssa wants to find out if the bread contains sugar.

(b) Name the solution that can be used to test for this.

.... (1)

(c) State the name of a solution Alyssa could use to see if starch is present in a sample.

.... (1)

(d) Alyssa carries out the emulsion test on one of her bread samples.
To start with she adds the bread sample and another substance
to a test tube, and shakes it until the bread dissolves.
(i) State the substance Alyssa would have added to the bread sample before shaking it.

.... (1)

(ii) At the end of the test, there is a milky emulsion.
State what this result shows about the sample.

.... (1)

(e) Describe how Alyssa would test a bread sample for protein. Include information about what would happen if protein is present.

....

....

.... (3)

/ 10

Drugs

Q1 Underline the statement below that is false.

All drugs are smoked.   **Drugs can affect behaviour.**

Drugs can damage your health.   **Drugs can be addictive.**   (1)

Q2 Some drugs are used for medical purposes.
Give one potential risk associated with medical drugs.

....

....   (1)

Q3 Tobacco is a recreational drug.

(a)   State what is meant by a recreational drug.

....   (1)

(b)   Explain one health risk of smoking tobacco.

....

....   (2)

(c)   Describe two potential negative effects of taking each of the following drugs:
(i)   Alcohol

1. ....

....

2. ....

....   (2)

(ii) Marijuana

1. ....

....

2. ....

....   (2)

/ 9

Preventing Disease

Q1 Viruses and bacteria can cause disease.

(a) (i) Give an example of a viral disease.

.... (1)

(ii) Give an example of a bacterial disease.

.... (1)

(b) Describe how viruses can make you feel ill.

....

.... (1)

Q2 Disease has a negative impact on human health and wellbeing.
Prevention is often the most effective way of stopping the spread of disease.

(a) Disease can be prevented by washing hands before eating.
Describe how this method acts as a defence against disease.

....

....

....

....

.... (2)

(b) Give one other example of cleanliness at a personal level that acts as a defence
against disease.

....

.... (1)

(c) Describe how one example of cleanliness at a community level helps
to prevent the spread of diseases.

....

....

.... (2)

/ 8

Breathing

Q1   The diagram shows the parallelogram model.

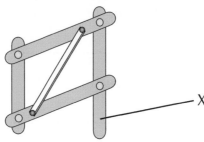

X

(a)   What does the rod labelled 'X' represent?

....   (1)

(b)   The diagram shows what the model looks like when the rubber band is stretched.
Describe what happens when the rubber band stops being stretched, and what this
represents in terms of a person's body.

....

....

....

....   (3)

Q2   The apparatus shown below is used to explain how the lungs work.

glass tubing

bell jar

balloons

rubber sheet

(a)   State the part of the apparatus that represents:
(i)   the lungs

....   (1)

(ii) the diaphragm

....   (1)

(iii) the chest cavity.

....   (1)

(b) When the rubber sheet is pulled down in the apparatus shown on the previous page, the balloons inflate. Explain why this happens.

....

....

.... (2)

Q3 Below is a diagram of the human gas exchange system.

A

B

(a) Name structure A.

.... (1)

(b) Name the muscle B.

.... (1)

(c) Explain what happens when muscle B contracts.

....

....

.... (3)

(d) Describe what happens when a person breathes out.

....

....

....

.... (3)

/ 17

More on Breathing

Q1 Jackson wants to know how much air he breathes out in a normal breath. He measures the volume of his exhaled breath five times using a measuring cylinder, a tank of water and a plastic tube. His results are shown in the table below.

Repeat	1	2	3	4	5
Volume (cm³)	450	525	470	485	415

(a) Calculate the mean volume of one of Jackson's exhaled breaths when breathing normally.

Mean volume = ... cm³   (1)

(b) Explain why it is important that Jackson takes several repeat measurements.

....

....   (2)

(c) State whether Jackson's results are precise. Explain your answer.

....

....   (1)

(d) A peak flow meter is shown on the right. Jackson's friend Kate wants to assess her vital capacity. Describe how she could use a peak flow meter to do this.

....

....   (2)

(e) Kate has asthma. Describe what may happen to her airways if she breathes in a substance that her airways are sensitive to.

....

....

....

....   (3)

(f) Emphysema is another condition that affects breathing. State one possible cause of this condition.

....   (1)

/ 10

Human Reproductive Systems

Q1 Underline the option that correctly completes the following sentences.

(a) In females, egg cells are released from the

ovaries   **fallopian tube**   **vagina**   **uterus**   (1)

(b) An egg cell is released every

14 days   **28 days**   **30 days**   **31 days**   (1)

Q2 The diagram shows the male reproductive system.

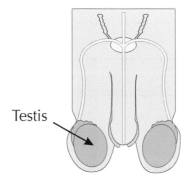

Testis

(a) Label the following structures on the diagram.

> **sperm duct**
> **urethra**

(2)

(b) Give one function of the urethra.

.... (1)

(c) Give the name of the male sex cells.

.... (1)

(d) Describe the function of the following structures in the male reproductive system.

(i) Testes:

.... (1)

(ii) Prostate gland:

.... (1)

Q3 The diagram below shows the female reproductive system.

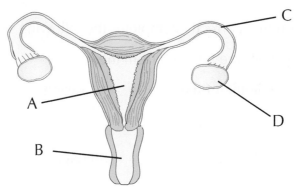

Name the feature each letter is labelling on the diagram.

A: ....

B: ....

C: ....

D: .... (4)

Q4 To have a baby, sperm need to be released inside the female.

(a) Describe how sexual intercourse brings sperm and eggs together.

....

....

.... (2)

(b) Compare the numbers of sperm and eggs released.

....

.... (1)

(c) Describe what happens when an egg is fertilised.

....

....

.... (2)

/ 17

Having a Baby

Q1 The diagram below shows a fetus attached to its mother.

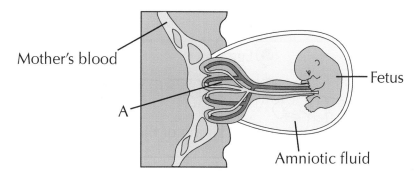

(a) State the name of the structure labelled A on the diagram.

.... (1)

(b) Describe the function of the amniotic fluid.

....

.... (1)

(c) Women are advised not to drink alcohol during pregnancy,
for the good of the growing fetus.

(i) How would alcohol get to the fetus?

....

....

.... (2)

(ii) State one negative effect that drinking alcohol during pregnancy
could have on the baby when it is born.

....

.... (1)

(d) At an earlier stage of development, the developing baby is called an embryo.
Describe how a fertilised egg becomes an embryo.

....

.... (1)

/ 6

Section B2 — Breathing and Reproduction

The Menstrual Cycle

Q1 The diagram below shows the main stages of the menstrual cycle.

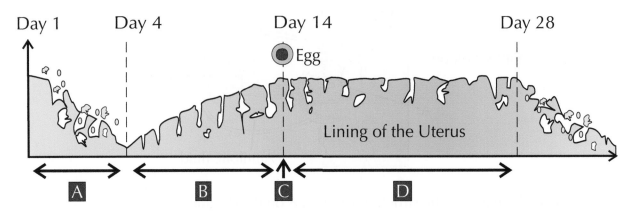

Day 1   Day 4   Day 14   Day 28

Egg

Lining of the Uterus

A   B   C   D

(a) Underline the letter that corresponds to each of the following stages of the menstrual cycle.

(i) The lining of the uterus builds up.

A   **B**   **C**   **D**   (1)

(ii) The thick lining of the uterus breaks down and blood flows out (menstruation).

A   **B**   **C**   **D**   (1)

(iii) The egg is travelling down the fallopian tube to be fertilised.

A   **B**   **C**   **D**   (1)

(iv) The lining of the uterus is very thick and full of blood.

A   **B**   **C**   **D**   (1)

(b) State why the lining of the uterus needs to become thick.

....

.... (1)

(c) Use the diagram to work out how long it takes the uterus lining to build up again after menstruation.

.... (1)

(d) State on which day of the menstrual cycle the egg is released.

.... (1)

/ 7

Section B2 — Breathing and Reproduction

Plant Reproduction, Fertilisation and Seed Dispersal

Q1 The picture below shows a flower. Some parts of the flower are labelled with letters.

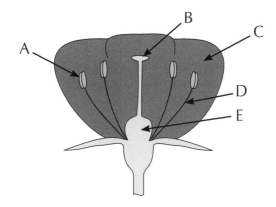

(a) State which letter points to the part that contains the female sex cells.

.... (1)

(b) State which letter points to the part that contains pollen grains.

.... (1)

(c) The plant is pollinated by insects.
    (i) Suggest one feature the flower might have to attract insects.

.... (1)

    (ii) Name the two parts of the flower that insects need to make
         contact with in order for pollination to occur.

    1. ....

    2. .... (2)

(d) Name another method that flowers can be pollinated by.
    Explain two adaptations a flower may have to be pollinated in this way.

Method: ....

Adaptation 1: ....

....

Adaptation 2: ....

.... (3)

Q2 Plants need to be pollinated to produce seeds.

(a) Describe the meaning of the term pollination.

....

.... (1)

(b) Describe what happens in a plant between pollination and fertilisation.

....

....

....

.... (3)

Q3 Plants have developed various seed dispersal methods.

(a) Explain the purpose of seed dispersal methods.

....

....

.... (2)

The pictures below show fruits from a tomato plant and a dandelion plant.

bright red skin

parachute

Tomato   Dandelion

(b) For each fruit, use the information in the picture to suggest whether each fruit is animal-dispersed or wind-dispersed. Explain your answers.

Tomato: ....

....

Dandelion: ....

.... (2)

(c) Describe one other method of seed dispersal a plant might use.

....

.... (1)

Q4 Some students investigated whether the size of sycamore fruit affects the distance to which the seeds are dispersed.
They made paper models of the fruits with different lengths of wings and dropped them from a height of 1 metre. There was a fan at a set distance behind the person dropping the models.

PRACTICAL

(a) State the type of seed dispersal the students are investigating.

.... (1)

(b) (i) Name the dependent variable in this experiment.

.... (1)

(ii) Name the independent variable in this experiment.

.... (1)

(c) The results of the experiment are shown in the graph below.

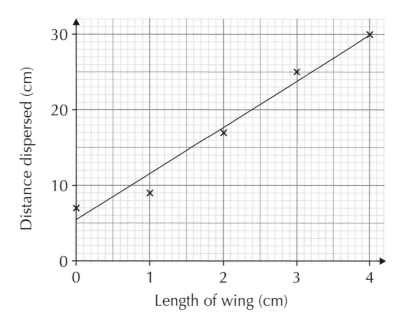

(i) Calculate how much further the model with the longest wings travelled than the one with no wings.

.... (1)

(ii) What can you conclude about the size of sycamore fruit and dispersal?

....

.... (1)

(d) Suggest how the students could make their results more reliable.

.... (1)

/ 23

Section B2 — Breathing and Reproduction

Plant Nutrition

Q1 Photosynthesis is a process that allows plants to produce food.

(a) For each part below, underline the option that completes the sentence.
  (i) One of the reactants in photosynthesis is

  hydrogen   **water**   **glucose**   **oxygen**   (1)

  (ii) The green chemical that allows plants to absorb sunlight is called

  carbon dioxide   **glucose**   **chlorophyll**   **nitrogen**   (1)

(b) Write the word equation that summarises what happens in photosynthesis.

.... (1)

(c) Explain one way plants use the food produced by photosynthesis.

.... (1)

Q2 Jill wants to see whether a chilli plant grows faster when watered once a week or twice a week. She decides to buy two chilli plants for her investigation. She finds the plants below at her local market.

> **PRACTICAL**

A   B   C   D   E

(a) State which two chilli plants she should use for her experiment.
Explain your answer.

Plants: ....

Reason: ....

.... (2)

(b) Describe a method Jill could use for her investigation.

....

....

.... (2)

/ 8

Photosynthesis Experiments

Q1 Anand is planning to carry out an investigation on photosynthesis in an aquatic plant. Anand says "as the intensity of light shining on the plant increases, the amount of light absorbed by the plant and used for photosynthesis also increases".

Anand carries out an experiment to measure the amount of oxygen produced by the plant over a period of 12 hours. He then uses his data to calculate the plant's average rate of photosynthesis. He repeats his experiment for different intensities of light whilst keeping all other variables constant. His results are shown in the graph on the right.

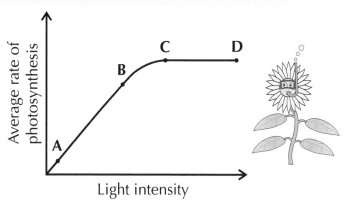

(a) State one way in which the data collected in the graph supports Anand's statement, and one way in which it does not.

Supports: ....

....

Does not support: ....

.... (2)

(b) Describe a simple method Anand could have used to measure the amount of oxygen produced by the aquatic plant over a period of 12 hours.

....

....

....

....

....

.... (4)

(c) (i) Explain why Anand keeps all other variables constant when he repeats the experiment for different light intensities.

.... (1)

(ii) Give two variables Anand should keep constant.

....

.... (2)

Q2 Tani decides to carry out an experiment to show whether the green colour of leaves is linked to starch production. She chooses a plant with variegated leaves.

(a) Name the chemical which makes area A green.

.... (1)

(b) Describe how plants use starch.

....

.... (1)

(c) Explain why Tani chooses a plant with variegated leaves.

....

.... (1)

Tani uses the iodine test to see where starch is present in the leaf. Iodine solution is brown.

(d) State what colour iodine solution changes to when it reacts with starch.

.... (1)

(e) Describe how Tani can prepare the leaf before it is tested with iodine solution.

....

....

....

.... (3)

(f) Suggest what colour each area (A and B) will be after testing the leaf with iodine solution. Explain your answer.

....

....

....

....

.... (2)

/ 18

The Importance of Plants

Q1 Underline the organism below that is able to photosynthesise.

    algae   **grasshopper**   **glow worm**   **snake** (1)

Q2 Some chickens are fed on grain from a crop grown in a nearby field. Explain how the crop uses the Sun's energy to become a source of energy for the chickens.

....

....

....

.... (3)

Q3 In the 18th century, Joseph Priestley conducted an important experiment in which he placed two mice in sealed bell jars. He also placed a plant in one of the jars.

PRACTICAL

Holes — Mouse A   Mouse B

Bell jar —

Plant

After a while, mouse A collapsed, while mouse B did not.

(a) Explain the results of this experiment.

....

....

....

....

.... (3)

(b) Explain how this experiment demonstrates the global importance of plants for life on Earth.

....

.... (1)

/ 8

Aerobic Respiration

Q1 A student is given a test tube of hydrogen carbonate indicator.   **PRACTICAL**

(a) Describe a method they could use to test exhaled air
for the main gas produced in aerobic respiration.

....

.... (1)

(b) Complete the table below to show the student's results.

Solution	Appearance without gas	Appearance with gas
Hydrogen carbonate indicator	Red	

(1)

Q2 Breathing and respiration are both essential for survival.

(a) Describe the two processes of breathing and respiration.

....

.... (2)

The diagram below shows a typical animal cell in which respiration takes place.

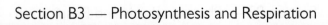

cytoplasm

nucleus

cell surface
membrane

mitochondria

(b) State the word equation for aerobic respiration.

.... (1)

(c) State where in the cell aerobic respiration takes place.

.... (1)

(d) Describe how the reactants for aerobic respiration are obtained
by the body and transported to cells for respiration to take place.

....

.... (2)

(e) Give one use of energy in the body.

.... (1)

/ 9

Section B3 — Photosynthesis and Respiration

Anaerobic Respiration

Q1 Organisms can respire aerobically and anaerobically.

(a) Describe the differences between aerobic respiration and anaerobic respiration in humans.

....

....

....

....

....

.... (3)

(b) Write the word equation for anaerobic respiration in plants.

.... (1)

Q2 Plant root cells need to respire just like all plant cells.

(a) Complete the passage below by choosing words from the box.

| slowly | aerobically | quickly | anaerobically |

In normal conditions spaces in the soil are filled with air. This means root cells

can respire .... If there is prolonged heavy rainfall, soils can

become waterlogged. This means the spaces in the soil fill up with water.

When this happens, root cells have to respire .... (2)

Mangrove trees grow along shores and rivers.
Many mangroves trees grow pencil-like roots,
that stick out of the water.

pencil-like root   trunk

(b) Suggest how this adaptation helps the mangrove trees release more energy from the glucose they store than if the roots were submerged underwater.

....

....

.... (2)

/ 8

PRACTICAL | # Fermentation

Q1 Emilia is doing an experiment to find out about yeast fermentation.
She places some yeast in warm water in an open bottle.

(a) State what else she will need to add to the bottle to make sure the yeast can respire.

.... (1)

(b) Emilia then attaches a balloon to the mouth of the bottle.
State what you expect to happen to the balloon. Explain your answer.

....

....

.... (3)

(c) Emilia says "This experiment helps to show you why bread rises and
why beer is fizzy." Explain how the experiment helps to show this.

....

....

....

....

.... (2)

(d) Emilia wants to extend her investigation to find out whether temperature affects
yeast fermentation. Describe a method she could use to investigate this.
State the variables she will need to control.

....

....

....

.... (4)

/ 10

Section B3 — Photosynthesis and Respiration

Interdependence and Food Webs

Q1 Complete the sentences below by underlining the best option.

Who's hungry?

(a) Organisms that can make their own food are called

carnivores   **herbivores**   **producers**   **consumers**   (1)

(b) An animal that only eats plants is a

secondary consumer   **top carnivore**   **primary consumer**   **producer**   (1)

Q2 A biologist is studying a coastal ecosystem. She draws the food chain below.

plankton ⟶ shrimp ⟶ herring ⟶ seagull

(a) Give the definition of an ecosystem.

....

....   (1)

(b) Name the tertiary consumer in this food chain.

....   (1)

The biologist wants to draw a food web for the coastal ecosystem.

(c) Give one difference between a food chain and a food web.

....

....   (1)

Here is some more information about organisms in the coastal ecosystem.

> Shrimps can be eaten by crabs.
> Herrings can be eaten by seals.
> Both seals and seagulls eat crabs.

(d) Use this information and the food chain above to draw a food web for
the coastal ecosystem.

(3)

Q3 A food web is shown.

(a) The organisms in this food web are interdependent. State what is meant by the term 'interdependent'.

....

....

.... (1)

(b) Write down the food chain that includes the weasel.

.... (1)

(c) (i) Name all of the species that are eaten by foxes.

.... (1)

(ii) Name the species which is eaten by two top carnivores and a secondary consumer.

.... (1)

(d) Suggest what might happen to the number of rabbits if the amount of grass increased. Explain your answer.

Result: ....

Explanation: .... (1)

(e) A disease kills all the mice. Explain one reason why the number of squirrels might increase and one reason why the number of squirrels might decrease.

....

....

....

....

....

....

....

.... (4)

/ 17

Section B4 — Interdependence and Populations

Investigating Populations

Q1 A student wants to investigate the number of woodlice in her garden.

(a) (i) Name a technique the student could use to capture woodlice for counting.

.... (1)

(ii) Describe how the technique given in (i) can be used to count woodlice.

....

....

.... (2)

(b) Suggest one way that the student could make sure her investigation produces reliable results.

.... (1)

Q2 A student is estimating the number of buttercups in his garden.

He uses the piece of equipment shown on the right.

(a) Name this piece of equipment.

.... (1)

The student places this piece of equipment at five random sample points in his garden.
He counts the number of buttercups inside the frame at each point.
His results are shown in this table.

Sample point	1	2	3	4	5
Number of buttercups	12	8	9	4	7

(b) Calculate the mean number of buttercups.

No. of buttercups = ... (2)

(c) The student works out that his garden has an area of 32 m².
The frame he used had an area of 1 m².
Calculate an estimate of the size of the population of buttercups in the garden.

Population size = ... (1)

/ 8

Protecting Living Things

Q1 Orang-utans live in the Indonesian rainforest.
They mostly eat fruit and leaves from the trees.

(a) A company wants to cut down a large area of rainforest in Indonesia.
Explain how this could affect the population size of the orang-utans.

....

....

....   (2)

(b) Use the words in the box to complete the paragraph below.
Each word may only be used once. You will not need to use all the words.

increasing	pollution	environment	conserving
living	generations	decreasing	habitats
sustainable	resources	organism	population

Humans use .... from the Earth to survive.

Human activity has led to .... of the environment and

damage to many .... The human population is

.... So we need to manage the way we use resources to

meet our needs without destroying things for future ....

— this is called .... development.   (6)

Q2 The Arabian oryx is hunted for its horns. In 1972 there were no longer any Arabian
oryx in the wild. Due to conservation work, there are now wild populations again.

(a) Some Arabian oryx are kept in captivity in zoos.
Explain how a zoo could help to conserve the wild Arabian oryx population.

....

....   (2)

(b) Suggest another conservation scheme that could be used to protect the oryx.

....   (1)

/ 11

Variation

Q1 The graph on the right shows the number of people who have each different blood group in a population.

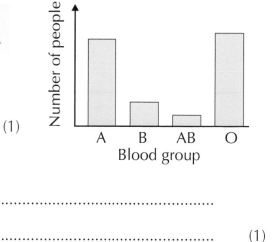

(a) State whether the variation shown by the graph is continuous or discontinuous.

.... (1)

(b) Explain your answer to part (a).

....

.... (1)

Q2 Toya's class are having a sunflower growing competition. She asks everyone in her class to record the height of their sunflower at the end of the competition.

Toya plots her results on the chart below.

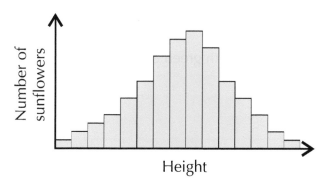

(a) Suggest two possible causes for the variation between the heights of sunflowers.

1. ....

....

2. ....

.... (2)

(b) (i) State whether the heights are an example of continuous or discontinuous variation.

.... (1)

(ii) Give two examples of this type of variation among the pupils of Toya's class.

1. ....

2. .... (2)

Q3 Eye colour and height show variation in humans. [PRACTICAL]

The eye colours of the students in two Year 7 classes were recorded in the table on the right.

(a) On the graph paper below, draw a bar chart of the results.

Eye colour	Number of students
Blue	7
Brown	37
Green	12
Other	4

(3)

(b) Calculate the percentage of students with green eyes.

.... % (1)

(c) A student wants to investigate the height variation in her class.

Suggest two things the student should do to make sure the height measurements she takes are accurate. Explain your reasoning for each point.

1. ....

....

....

2. ....

....

.... (4)

/ 15

Classification

Q1 Living things are divided into five kingdoms.

Plants, animals and fungi are three of the five kingdoms.
Name the other two kingdoms.

1. ....

2. .... (2)

Q2 Two arthropods, A and B, are shown on the right.

(a) (i) Name the group of arthropods that A belongs to.

.... (1)

(ii) State one feature of A that allows you to identify the group it belongs to.

.... (1)

(b) (i) Name the group of arthropods that B belongs to.

.... (1)

(ii) State one feature of B that allows you to identify the group it belongs to.

.... (1)

Q3 The photograph below shows organism A in its natural habitat.

(a) Name the kingdom that organism A belongs to.

.... (1)

(b) Name the group of vertebrates
that organism A belongs to.

.... (1)

scaly skin

organism A's
eggs

sand

(c) *Canis Latrans* prey on vertebrates like organism A. *Canis Latrans* are
warm-blooded creatures, with sharp claws, thick brown fur and a long tail.
Identify the group of vertebrates that *Canis Latrans* belong to.

.... (1)

/ 9

Structures of Different Organisms

Q1 Organisms in the five different kingdoms have different structures and life processes.

(a) Complete the table below.

Kingdom	Single-celled?	Cells have a nucleus?	Cells have a cell wall?	Able to move around?
Animals	No	....	No	Yes
....	Can be	Yes	Yes	....
Plants	No	Yes	....	No

(2)

(b) Some kingdoms contain organisms that are able to make their own food. Name two of these kingdoms.

1. ....

2. .... (2)

Q2 The photograph below shows a penguin, which belongs to the bird group. Penguins have a number of structures which help them to survive and reproduce.

(a) Penguins have webbed feet. Suggest one advantage to the penguin of having webbed feet.

....

.... (1)

(b) Using the photograph above, identify one other structure of a penguin and suggest how it helps the penguin to survive or reproduce.

....

....

.... (2)

/ 7

The Particle Model

Q1 Solids, liquids and gases can be represented using the particle model.

(a) Name the state of matter that is represented by the particles shown on the right. Explain your reasoning.

State of matter: ....

Reasoning: ....

.... (2)

(b) In terms of the particle model, explain why solids keep a definite shape, whereas liquids and gases take the shape of their container.

....

....

....

.... (4)

Q2 The diagram below shows two sealed syringes.
Each syringe contains the same volume of air or water.

Syringe A   seal↓   air

Syringe B   plunger↓   water

(a) Assume that air and water particles are the same size.
State which syringe contains the larger number of particles. Explain your answer.

....

.... (2)

(b) (i) Suggest a way of increasing the volume of the air in syringe A without changing the number of air particles.

.... (1)

(ii) Suggest whether it would be possible to increase the volume of the water in a similar way. Explain your answer.

....

.... (1)

/ 10

Changes of State

Q1 A substance can change state between a solid, a liquid and a gas.

(a) Name the changes of state that are labelled A - C in the diagram below.

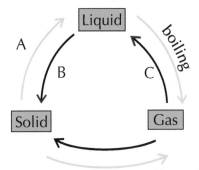

A: .... (1)

B: .... (1)

C: .... (1)

(b) A substance can change state from a liquid to a gas by boiling or evaporation. Describe how evaporation differs from boiling.

....

....

.... (2)

Q2 The diagram below shows an experiment that was set up to investigate the sublimation of iodine.

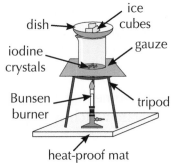

(a) Complete the sentences below:

(i) When heated, iodine will change state from

a .... to a .... (1)

(ii) When cooled, iodine will change state from

a .... to a .... (1)

(b) (i) Describe what happens to the particles of iodine when cooled.

....

.... (2)

(ii) Explain your answer to part (i).

....

....

.... (2)

/ 11

Section C1 — States of Matter

Gas Pressure and Diffusion

Q1 Inflatable mattresses are filled with air. The air particles create a gas pressure within the mattress.

(a) Describe how the air particles create pressure in the mattress.

....

.... (1)

(b) Suggest what will happen to the pressure in the mattress if more air is pumped into it. Explain your answer.

....

....

.... (2)

Q2 Ena was investigating whether the rate of diffusion in a liquid depends on the temperature of the liquid.

PRACTICAL

She set up an experiment as shown below.

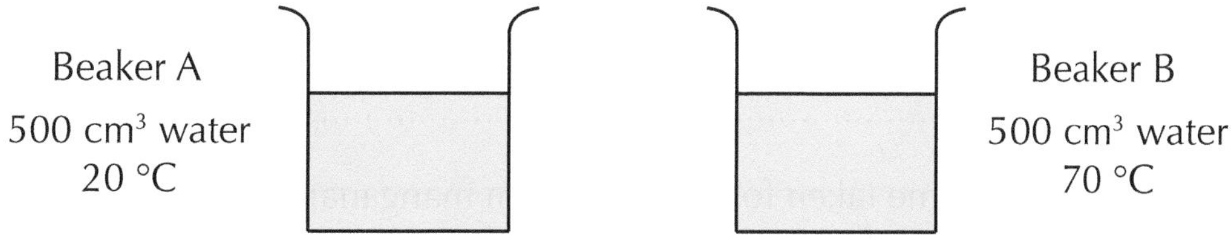

Beaker A
500 cm³ water
20 °C

Beaker B
500 cm³ water
70 °C

A large crystal of potassium manganate(VII) was added to beaker A and beaker B.

Ena then timed how long it took for the potassium manganate(VII) to completely diffuse through the water.

She then repeated the experiment two more times.

(a) Explain what is meant by the diffusion of potassium manganate(VII) in terms of particles.

....

....

....

.... (2)

(b) The diffusion of potassium manganate(VII) occurs slowly. Explain why.

....

.... (1)

(c) For the experiment outlined on the previous page, underline:

(i) the independent variable

| water temperature | time taken for potassium manganate(VII) to diffuse | mass of potassium manganate(VII) | rate of diffusion | (1) |

(ii) the dependent variable

| water temperature | time taken for potassium manganate(VII) to diffuse | mass of potassium manganate(VII) | rate of diffusion | (1) |

(iii) a control variable

| water temperature | time taken for potassium manganate(VII) to diffuse | mass of potassium manganate(VII) | rate of diffusion | (1) |

The results of the experiment are shown below.

Beaker	Time (s)			
	Experiment 1	**Experiment 2**	**Experiment 3**	**Mean**
A	279	251	232	254
B	108	134	127	

(d) Repeating the experiment three times and taking a mean can help to judge how precise the results are. Describe two other advantages of repeating the experiment.

1. ....

2. .... (2)

(e) Calculate the mean time taken for the potassium manganate(VII) to completely diffuse in beaker B. Show your working.

Time = ... s (1)

(f) Use the results to write a conclusion for this experiment.

....

....

.... (2)

(g) Suggest one improvement Ena could make to her method to further investigate the relationship between temperature and the rate of diffusion.

.... (1)

/ 15

Atoms and Elements

Q1 Underline the correct option to complete the sentences below.

(a) Different elements contain...

...the same type of atom.

...the same type of compound.

...different types of atom.

...different types of compound.

(1)

(b) The elements are organised in the

elemental table   **daltonic table**   **chemical table**   **periodic table** (1)

(c) The number of known elements is approximately

100   **300**   **1000**   **1500**   (1)

Q2 Give the chemical symbol of each of the following elements.

(a) carbon

.... (1)

(b) chlorine

.... (1)

(c) calcium

.... (1)

(d) copper

.... (1)

Q3 All matter is made up of atoms.

(a) Describe what an atom is.

.... (1)

(b) Describe what an element is.

....

.... (1)

/ 9

Compounds

Q1 The particles in four different substances are shown below.

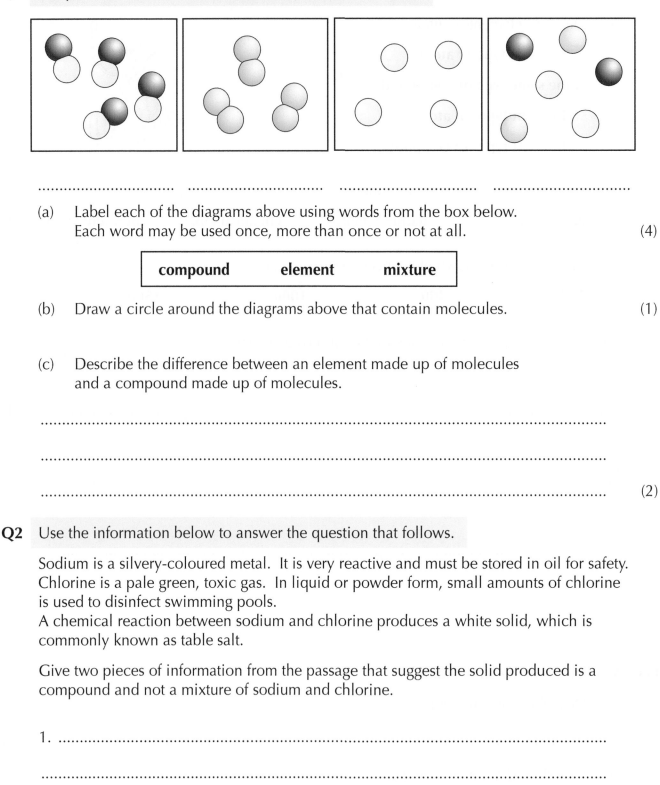

....

(a) Label each of the diagrams above using words from the box below.
Each word may be used once, more than once or not at all. (4)

> **compound**   **element**   **mixture**

(b) Draw a circle around the diagrams above that contain molecules. (1)

(c) Describe the difference between an element made up of molecules
and a compound made up of molecules.

....

....

.... (2)

Q2 Use the information below to answer the question that follows.

Sodium is a silvery-coloured metal. It is very reactive and must be stored in oil for safety.
Chlorine is a pale green, toxic gas. In liquid or powder form, small amounts of chlorine
is used to disinfect swimming pools.
A chemical reaction between sodium and chlorine produces a white solid, which is
commonly known as table salt.

Give two pieces of information from the passage that suggest the solid produced is a
compound and not a mixture of sodium and chlorine.

1. ....

....

2. ....

.... (2)

/ 9

Chemical Formulae

Q1 Give the chemical formulae of the following compounds.

(a) sodium hydroxide

.... (1)

(b) sulfuric acid

.... (1)

Q2 Three substances are shown below. The diagrams include
the chemical symbols of the elements in each substance.

A

O
O

B

H O
H

C

Ca O
C
O O

State the name of each of these substances.

A: ....

B: ....

C: .... (3)

Q3 State the name of the compound formed from the following reactants.

(a) sodium and chlorine

.... (1)

(b) iron and sulfur

.... (1)

Q4 A compound is made up of one carbon atom and four hydrogen atoms.

(a) Write the chemical formula of this compound.

.... (1)

(b) Name this compound.

.... (1)

/ 9

      Section C2 — Atoms, Elements, Molecules and Compounds

Properties of Metals and Non-Metals

Q1 Complete the sentences below by underlining the best option.

(a) An element that you would expect to be a gas at room temperature is

copper   **mercury**   **helium**   **aluminium**   (1)

(b) An element that you would expect to be a solid at room temperature is

bromine   **chlorine**   **zinc**   **neon**   (1)

Q2 Use the words in the box to fill in the gaps in the paragraph below.

scrub	**strong**	**conduct**	**forces**	**weak**

Graphite, made from the element carbon, is used in making the 'lead' in pencils.

In graphite, the .... between the particles are ....

Graphite wears away quickly because it's easy to .... atoms off it.   (3)

Q3 John investigated the properties of a mystery substance called "Q". The table below shows the results of the tests (A – D) that he did on the substance.

Q→

Test	Description of Test	Result
A	Attach Q in an electric circuit with a light bulb	No light
B	Bend Q	Cracks appear
C	Hold Q in a Bunsen burner flame	Starts to melt
D	Hold Q near a bar magnet	No attraction

(a) State whether substance Q is a metal or a non-metal.

.... (1)

(b) Name the physical property that is being tested in test B.

.... (1)

(c) Explain the result of test A.

....

....

.... (2)

Q4 Layla has three different samples of substances.

> Sample 1 is a dull red colour. It's an electrical insulator and has a low melting point.
>
> Sample 2 is a shiny brownish orange colour. It has a high melting point and can be hammered into sheets.
>
> Sample 3 shatters when dropped on the floor. It isn't magnetic and has a low boiling point.

(a) Give the sample(s) that are non-metals.

.... (1)

(b) Give the sample(s) that are metals.

.... (1)

(c) Explain whether you would expect sample 2 to be an electrical conductor or an electrical insulator.

....

....

.... (2)

Q5 Saucepans are normally made out of metal.

(a) Describe one property of metals that makes them suitable materials for saucepans.

....

....

.... (2)

(b) Some saucepans have a handle made out of non-metal.
Explain why a person may prefer to use a saucepan like this.

....

....

....

.... (3)

46

Q6 Gwen has three small rods labelled A, B and C.
The rods are made of iron, aluminium and graphite,
but she doesn't know which rod is made of which material.

Gwen tests the electrical conductivity of the three rods.

(a) State whether she will be able to identify any of the materials
using this test alone. Give a reason for your answer.

....

....

.... (2)

(b) Describe an experiment that she could carry out to see
which of the materials is the best conductor of heat.

....

....

....

....

....

....

.... (4)

Gwen then tries to bend each of the three rods. Her results are shown in the table.

Rod	Result
A	No change
B	The rod snaps
C	No change

(c) Identify the material that makes up rod B.

.... (1)

Gwen then tests rods A and C with a bar magnet. Only rod C is attracted to the magnet.

(d) Identify the materials that make up rod A and C.

Rod A: ....

Rod C: .... (1)

/ 26

Section C2 — Atoms, Elements, Molecules and Compounds   ✓   ✓   ✓

Purity and Mixtures

Q1   Becky reads several reliable sources that tell her
the melting point of pure citric acid is 153 °C.

(a)   Underline the option below that completes the following sentence.

A pure substance is always made up of...

...particles of only one element.

...particles of only one element or one compound.

...particles of only one compound.

...particles of two or more compounds.   (1)

(b)   Becky's teacher gives her a sample of citric acid which is a white solid.
She tests the melting point of the solid and finds that it melts
over a range of temperatures, from 148 °C to 154 °C.
Suggest why the melting point of Becky's sample isn't 153 °C.

....

....   (1)

Q2   Arjun dissolves some sugar in some water to make a clear solution.

(a)   Describe what happens to the molecules of sugar when the sugar dissolves
in the water. In your answer, you should include a description of
how the sugar particles are distributed within the water.

....

....

....

....   (3)

Arjun says that he needs to carry out a chemical reaction to get the sugar back.

(b)   Explain why Arjun is incorrect.

....

....

....   (2)

(c)   Use what you know about mixtures to suggest why sugar water tastes sweet.

....

....   (1)

Q3 Tanner has a sample of three different solid substances. | PRACTICAL |

(a) Describe a method Tanner could use to
measure the melting point of each sample.

....

....

.... (2)

Tanner's results are shown in the table below.

Sample	Melting point (°C)
A	51 - 63
B	31 - 32
C	69

(b) Suggest which of the three samples is pure. Explain your answer.

....

.... (2)

One of the three substances is stearic acid, which has a melting point of 69 °C,
one substance is capric acid, which has a melting point of 32 °C,
and one is candle wax, which is a mixture of different substances.

(c) Identify which sample is most likely to be capric acid
and explain what the result suggests about the sample's purity.

....

....

.... (2)

Tanner then measures the melting point of a sample of a different type of candle wax.
It has a melting point of 46 - 55 °C. This melting point range does not match
that of the original candle wax sample.

(d) Suggest one reason why this might be.

....

....

.... (1)

/ 15

Air

Q1 Air is a mixture of gases.

(a) State what is meant by the term mixture.

....

.... (1)

(b) The pie chart below shows the composition of the air.

other gases (1%)

gas X
21%

gas Y
78%

(i) Name gas X.

.... (1)

(ii) Name gas Y.

.... (1)

(iii) Name one of the other gases that is found in air.

.... (1)

(iv) Name the gas found in air that is an important reactant in respiration.

.... (1)

Q2 Tony soaks some iron wool in water and pushes it into a test tube. He covers the end of the tube with his thumb and puts the tube upside down in a beaker of water. The iron wool begins to rust.

PRACTICAL

Describe how he could use this set-up to show what proportion of air is oxygen.

....

....

....

....

....

.... (3)

/ 8

Properties of Water

Q1 Choose words from the box to complete the passage below.

more	less	increases	decreases

When most substances freeze, their particles get closer together.

This makes the substances .... dense. When water freezes,

the particles get further apart. So ice is .... dense than liquid water.

This means that when you freeze water it .... in volume. (3)

Q2 Ellen did an experiment to compare the amount of other substances present in seawater, tap water and distilled water. The method that she used is shown in the box below.

 PRACTICAL

> 1. Weigh an empty evaporating dish and record its mass.
> 2. Measure out 30 ml of seawater into the dish.
> 3. Heat the dish gently until all the water has evaporated.
> 4. Weigh the dish again to find the mass of any solids left in the dish.
> 5. Repeat steps 1-4 using tap water, then distilled water.

(a) Explain why Ellen used the same volume of each of the three types of water.

.... (1)

(b) The table below shows the results of Ellen's experiment. Complete the second column of the table to show which type of water was in each dish.

Dish	Type of water	Mass of solid left in dish (g)
1	....	1.06
2	....	0.03
3	....	0.00

(2)

Nat does the experiment but boils off half the water, then leaves the dish in a warm place. Ellen says that the rest of the water will not be removed because it is no longer boiling.

(c) Discuss whether Ellen is correct.

....

....

.... (1)

/ 7

Distillation

Q1 Callum has some blackcurrant squash. He uses the apparatus shown below to extract some pure water from the squash.

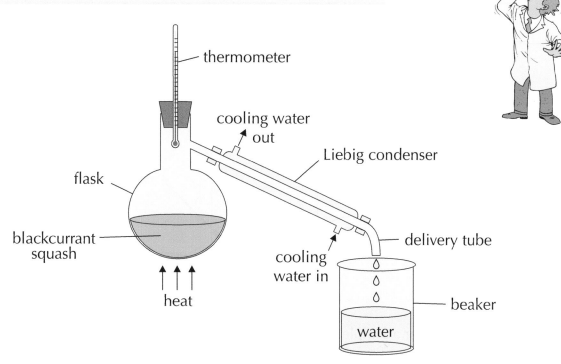

(a) Explain how the Liebig condenser turns the water vapour back into liquid water as it leaves the flask.

....

....

.... (1)

(b) Explain why the end of the delivery tube should not be below the surface of the water in the beaker after the heat has been turned off.

....

.... (1)

(c) Apart from a decrease in volume, state what change you would expect Callum to observe in the liquid in the flask over the course of his experiment. Explain your answer.

Observation: ....

Explanation: ....

.... (2)

/ 4

Chromatography

Q1 Label the chromatography equipment with the words in the box.

| chromatography paper | baseline | beaker | solvent | lid | ink spot |

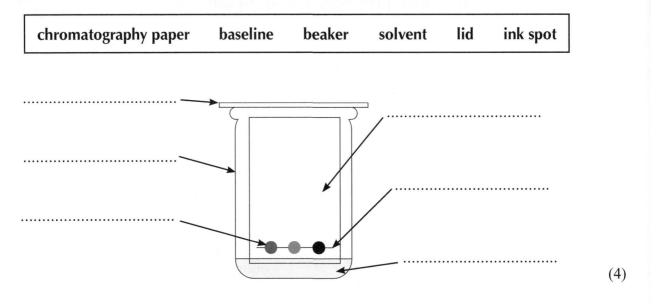

....

....

....

....

....

....

(4)

Q2 Eve's teacher gave her a sample of the ink from a felt tip pen. She used chromatography to work out which one of four pens, **A**, **B**, **C** or **D**, the ink sample was taken from.

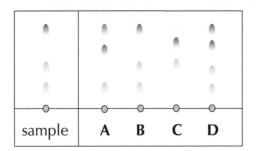

(a) State the minimum number of dyes the ink sample contained.

.... (1)

(b) State which pen the sample was taken from. Explain your answer.

Pen: ....

Reason: .... (2)

(c) Suggest why the baseline has to be drawn in pencil and not pen.

....

.... (1)

/ 8

Section C3 — Purity, Mixtures and Separating Mixtures

Chemical Reactions

Q1 Underline the option that completes the following sentence about chemical reactions.

During a chemical reaction...

...atoms are created and destroyed.

...there is no change in energy.

...atoms are rearranged.

...all of the bonds between atoms stay the same.   (1)

Q2 When oxygen and hydrogen react together they form water.

Write a word equation for the reaction.

....   (1)

Q3 The ripening of bananas is an example of a chemical reaction. **PRACTICAL**
Billie's father tells her that if bananas are placed in a sealed
container, they will ripen more quickly than if left on the counter.

Billie decides to test this. She seals one unripened bunch of bananas
in a container, and leaves another unripened bunch out on the counter.

(a)   State one control variable in this experiment.

....   (1)

As bananas ripen, they develop brown spots. After three days, Billie opens the container
and removes the bananas. The two bunches of bananas are shown below.

bananas kept
on counter

bananas kept
in container

(b)   Write a conclusion for this experiment.

....

....

....

....   (2)

/ 5

More on Reactions and Using Bunsen Burners

Q1 Shanti heats some white lead carbonate powder with a Bunsen burner. She uses the apparatus below. After a while, the powder turns yellow.

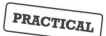

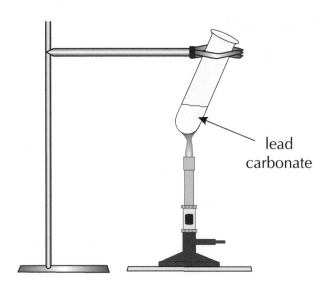

lead carbonate

(a) Shanti measures the total mass of the test tube and powder before and after the reaction. Her results are shown in the table below.

Mass before (g)	Mass after (g)
40.0	39.3

Calculate the difference in mass.

Difference in mass = ... g   (1)

(b) Suggest why the mass has decreased.

....

....   (1)

(c) Explain why mass is always conserved in a chemical reaction.

....

....   (1)

(d) Shanti is concerned about the effect of random error on her results.
Suggest what she could do to reduce the effect of random error on her results.

....

....   (1)

Q2 Tom is doing an experiment which involves heating some chemicals in a test tube. The method tells him to heat the reaction "gently", so he uses a Bunsen burner set to a medium blue flame.  **PRACTICAL**

(a) Describe how Tom should set the air hole on a Bunsen burner to get a medium blue flame.

.... (1)

(b) Underline the option that completes the sentence about Bunsen burners below.

Closing the air hole of the Bunsen burner...

...decreases the temperature of the flame because it increases the amount of air entering the burner.

...decreases the temperature of the flame because it decreases the amount of air entering the burner.

...increases the temperature of the flame because it increases the amount of air entering the burner.

...increases the temperature of the flame because it decreases the amount of air entering the burner. (1)

(c) After heating the test tube, Tom sets the Bunsen burner to the safety flame.
(i) What colour is the safety flame?

.... (1)

(ii) Suggest two other safety precautions that Tom should take when he uses a Bunsen burner.

1. ....

2. .... (2)

(d) The diagram below shows the roaring blue flame of a Bunsen burner.

On the diagram, draw a circle around the hottest point of the roaring blue flame. (1)

/ 10

 Section C4 — Combustion and Thermal Decomposition

Combustion

Q1 Combustion is a type of chemical reaction.

Use the words and phrases in the box below to complete the following sentences about combustion.

a bike rusting	burns	chocolate melting	a bonfire
melts	water freezing	freezes	rusts

Combustion is when a substance ....

in oxygen to release energy.

An example of a combustion reaction is ....   (2)

Q2 When there is enough heat and oxygen, hydrocarbons combust to produce energy.

(a) Explain what is meant by the term 'hydrocarbon'.

....   (1)

(b) Complete the word equation below to show the products that form when hydrocarbons combust.

hydrocarbon + oxygen $\longrightarrow$

.... + ... (+ energy)   (1)

Q3 The diagram below shows a burning splint.

Flame _____   Wooden splint

(a) Heat and oxygen are required for the splint to continue burning. State the third necessary requirement for the flame to continue burning along the splint.

....   (1)

(b) The flame is blown out so that the splint is just glowing.
Describe how the splint can now be used to test for the presence of oxygen.

....

....   (1)

Section C4 — Combustion and Thermal Decomposition

Q4 Bella uses the apparatus below to test whether a candle produces carbon dioxide. Any gas released by the candle will pass through the limewater.

PRACTICAL

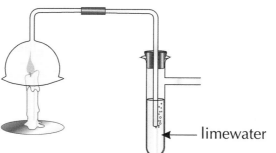

limewater

Explain how Bella will know whether carbon dioxide is produced by the candle.

.... (1)

Q5 A student uses a Bunsen burner to burn carbon in air. The diagram below shows the reaction that takes place.

$$C \ + \ O\,O \ \longrightarrow \ O\,C\,O$$

Write a word equation for the reaction.

.... (1)

Q6 Zara uses a Bunsen burner to investigate the combustion of magnesium. **PRACTICAL**

(a) Describe what she will observe.

.... (1)

(b) Give one safety precaution that she should take, specific to this reaction.

.... (1)

Q7 A scientist uses a Bunsen burner to burn sulfur in air. **PRACTICAL**
It produces a small blue flame.

(a) State the product of this reaction.

.... (1)

(b) The scientist then places the burning sulfur into a jar of oxygen. Suggest what they would observe. Explain your answer.

....

....

.... (2)

/ 13

Section C4 — Combustion and Thermal Decomposition

The Effects of Fossil Fuels

Q1 Burning fossil fuels releases carbon dioxide and water vapour into the atmosphere.

(a) State two other products that are released when there is a limited oxygen supply.

.... (2)

(b) Explain how burning fossil fuels that contain sulfur impurities can cause acid rain.

....

....

....

.... (2)

Q2 Burning fossil fuels releases carbon dioxide and can have a negative impact on the environment.

The graph below shows how the amount of carbon dioxide in the atmosphere has changed over time.

Amount of carbon dioxide in the atmosphere (%)

0.034
0.032
0.030
0.028

1850   1900   1950   2000
Year

(a) Describe the trend in the amount of carbon dioxide in the atmosphere shown by the graph.

.... (1)

(b) Keisha thinks that the average global temperature will have increased over the same time period. Explain why she might think this.

....

....

.... (2)

(c) Suggest one way we can reduce the level of carbon dioxide in the atmosphere.

.... (1)

/ 8

Section C4 — Combustion and Thermal Decomposition

Thermal Decomposition Reactions

Q1 When hydrated copper sulfate is heated, it forms anhydrous copper sulfate and water.

PRACTICAL

(a) State the colour of anhydrous copper sulfate.

.... (1)

(b) A student has a sample of anhydrous copper sulfate.
He adds water to the sample. Describe the colour change he would observe.

.... (1)

Q2 A student heated copper carbonate, as shown in the diagram below.
It changed colour from green to black and a gas was given off.

PRACTICAL

copper carbonate

HEAT

(a) Give the name of the black product.

.... (1)

(b) Name the gas produced by the reaction.

.... (1)

(c) Write a word equation for this reaction.

.... (1)

Q3 When calcium carbonate is heated, a chemical reaction takes place.

(a) Name the two products of this reaction.

1. ....

2. .... (2)

(b) Name one substance that does not change chemically when heated.

.... (1)

/ 8

Section C4 — Combustion and Thermal Decomposition

Reactions of Metals with Oxygen and Water

Q1 Callum investigated the reactions of three unknown metals — A, B and C. He set up three test tubes, each containing a sample of one of the metals. He then added some water to each test tube and recorded whether a reaction took place. If a reaction didn't take place, he tested the metal to see if it would react with steam. His results are shown below.

Test tube	Metal	Reaction with water?	Reaction with steam?
1	A	yes	-
2	B	no	no
3	C	no	yes

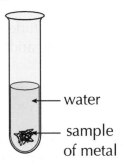

← water

← sample of metal

(a)   Using Callum's results, put metals A, B and C in order from most to least reactive.

Most reactive   Least reactive

.... , ... , ...   (1)

(b)   A gas was produced by the reaction in test tube 1.
(i)   State the name of this gas.

....   (1)

(ii)   Describe a test that Callum could carry out to show that this gas is produced.

....

....   (2)

(c)   Metal C didn't react with water but it did react with steam.
State the two products that are formed when a metal reacts with steam.

....   (1)

Q2 Rayna is investigating the reactions of different metals with oxygen.

(a)   State what type of reaction this is.

....   (1)

(b)   Underline the correct word to complete the sentence below.

Most metals react with oxygen to form a metal...

...carbonate.   **...oxide.**   **...hydroxide.**   **...sulfate.**   (1)

/ 7

Oxidation — Rusting

Q1 Anan builds a bird table in his garden using iron nails. After two weeks, he observes that the colour of the nails has changed from shiny grey to a dull brown.

(a) Complete the word equation for the reaction that has taken place.

iron + oxygen + water ⟶ .... (1)

(b) State the name given to the type of reaction observed by Anan.

.... (1)

(c) Describe how Anan could set up an experiment using three identical nails and three test tubes to show that both oxygen and water are needed for rust to form.

....

....

....

.... (2)

Q2 Misty owns a chainsaw with an iron chain. She leaves the chainsaw outside. After a week, she discovers that the chain has started to rust.

(a) Explain why the chain has started to rust.

.... (1)

Misty buys a new chain. She decides to oil the chain to prevent it from rusting.

(b) Explain why oiling is a suitable method for protecting an iron chain from rusting.

....

.... (2)

(c) State one other way to protect iron from rusting.

.... (1)

/ 8

Section C5 — Oxidation Reactions, Acids and Alkalis

PRACTICAL

Acids and Alkalis

Q1 Jan tested some substances around her home with Universal indicator solution.

Her results are shown in the table below.

Substance	Universal indicator colour
Lemon juice	Red
Drain cleaner	Purple
Washing up liquid	Blue
Rain water	Yellow

(a) Name the substance in the table that is a strong alkali.

.... (1)

(b) Suggest the pH value of lemon juice.

.... (1)

(c) Jan wants to know if vinegar is an acid.
Describe how she could use litmus paper to test for acidity.

....

.... (2)

Q2 Alan wants to know the pH of the soil in his garden. He takes soil samples from six randomly chosen points in his garden and tests the pH with a pH meter.

His results are shown in the table below.

Sample site	1	2	3	4	5	6
Soil pH	7.2	7.8	7.0	7.7	8.0	8.5

(a) Calculate the mean (average) pH of the soil samples.

Mean pH = ... (1)

(b) Identify the sample site that had soil with a neutral pH.

.... (1)

(c) Alan adds a few drops of Universal indicator to the sample of soil from site 6.
State the colour that the indicator will turn.

.... (1)

(d) Alan wants to plant some flowers that prefer a slightly acidic soil.
Predict whether these flowers will grow well in his garden. Explain your answer.

....

.... (1)

/ 8

Neutralisation

Q1 Underline the option that correctly completes the sentence about neutralisation reactions.

A neutralisation reaction...

...is a reaction between two substances with a neutral pH.

...is a reaction that produces products with a neutral pH.

...is a reaction between two acids.

...is a reaction that produces an acid and a base. (1)

Q2 Zhen wants to make some salts using neutralisation reactions.

State what acid she could use to produce each of the salts below.

copper sulfate: ....

magnesium nitrate: ....

zinc chloride: .... (3)

Q3 Inderjit is making salt crystals in the laboratory. His experiment is shown below.

PRACTICAL

(a) He adds the base using a dropper, and tests the solution after every few drops until all the acid has been neutralised. What colour does the Universal indicator paper turn when all the acid has been neutralised?

.... (1)

(b) The salt formed during this reaction is potassium nitrate. State the other product of the neutralisation reaction.

.... (1)

Section C5 — Oxidation Reactions, Acids and Alkalis

64

Q4 When a metal carbonate reacts with an acid a salt is formed.

(a) Complete the word equation below to show all the products formed when a metal carbonate reacts with an acid.

metal carbonate + acid →

   salt + ... + ... (2)

(b) Name the salt formed during each of the reactions below.

calcium carbonate + sulfuric acid: ....

sodium carbonate + hydrochloric acid: ....

magnesium carbonate + nitric acid: .... (3)

Q5 A salt solution can be made by neutralising hydrochloric acid with sodium hydroxide solution. The method for this reaction is shown below.

| PRACTICAL |

1. Add 1 cm³ of sodium hydroxide solution to a test tube containing 20 cm³ of hydrochloric acid.
2. Remove a small sample of the solution in the test tube and check to see if the pH is neutral.
3. Repeat this process until you have a neutral solution.

(a) Name the salt formed during this reaction.

.... (1)

(b) Suggest one safety precaution you should take when working with acids and alkalis.

.... (1)

Kevin decides to carry out this experiment, but adds 5 cm³ of alkali in step 1, rather than 1 cm³. He measures the pH with a digital pH meter and records his results in the table below.

Volume of alkali added (cm³)	0	5	10	15	20
pH of solution	1.0	1.0	1.5	2.0	9.0

(c) Kevin evaporates the water from the resulting solution. Explain why this will not produce a pure sample of salt.

....

....

.... (2)

/ 15

Section C5 — Oxidation Reactions, Acids and Alkalis

Reactions of Metals with Acids

Q1 Josh put some aluminium in a flask with some dilute hydrochloric acid. He collected the gas produced by the reaction and recorded the total volume of gas given off at regular intervals. His results are shown in the table below.

Time (s)	Volume of gas (cm³)
0	0
10	1.6
20	2.8
30	3.6
40	4.0
50	4.0

(a) Draw a graph of his results on the grid below. Include a curved line of best fit.

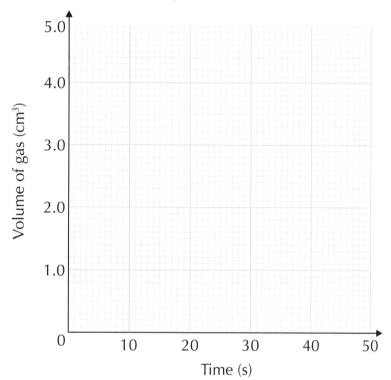

(2)

(b) Name the products formed in this reaction.

.... (2)

The more vigorously a metal and acid react, the faster the rate of gas production.

(c) Josh has five metals, all of equal size. Describe how he could use this method to find out which of the five metals is the most reactive.

....

.... (2)

/ 6

            Section C5 — Oxidation Reactions, Acids and Alkalis

Reactions of Oxides with Acids

Q1 Underline the substance below that could be used to neutralise a solution of sulfur dioxide.

water (pH 7)

citric acid (pH 2)

sodium hydroxide solution (pH 14)

rain water (pH 5)

(1)

Q2 Metal and non-metal oxides can take part in neutralisation reactions.

(a) Complete the sentence below by underlining the correct options.

Metal oxide solutions have a pH which is **higher** / **lower** than 7 so they are **acidic** / **alkaline**.

(1)

(b) State the two products formed when a metal oxide solution is neutralised.

.... (1)

(c) A metal oxide and a non-metal oxide are dissolved in separate beakers of water. Which solution would give the higher value when measured with a pH meter?

.... (1)

Q3 Josie carries out an experiment in which magnesium burns in oxygen.

(a) Write a word equation for the reaction of magnesium with oxygen.

.... (1)

(b) Josie dissolves some of the product of this reaction in water.
Suggest a pH value for this solution.

.... (1)

(c) Josie then adds dilute sulfuric acid to the solution.
(i) Name the type of reaction that will take place.

.... (1)

(ii) Name the salt formed during this reaction.

.... (1)

/ 8

Section C5 — Oxidation Reactions, Acids and Alkalis

Limestone

Q1 The photograph below shows a natural limestone pavement.

(a) Give the name of the main compound that makes up limestone.

.... (1)

(b) Blocks of limestone can be used to construct buildings.
    (i) Suggest a disadvantage of constructing buildings out of limestone.

.... (1)

    (ii) Give two other uses of limestone in the construction of buildings.

1. ....

2. .... (2)

(c) State the three products of the reaction between limestone and hydrochloric acid.

1. ....

2. ....

3. .... (3)

Q2 Agricultural lime can be applied to fields to alter the pH of the soil.

(a) (i) State the effect agricultural lime has on soil pH.

.... (1)

    (ii) Name the type of reaction that causes this effect.

.... (1)

(b) Describe how agricultural lime is produced.

....

.... (2)

/ 11

Acids and the Environment

Q1 Rain water is naturally acidic.

(a) Name the gas that dissolves in rain water to make carbonic acid.

.... (1)

There are other gases in the atmosphere which contribute to acid rain.

(b) Name one of these gases.

.... (1)

(c) George wants to buy a statue for his garden.
The first shop he goes to has the two statues below.

A

B

Limestone   Magnesium

George decides that neither of the statues would be suitable for his garden.
Explain how he came to this decision.

....

....

....

.... (3)

Q2 Marble is a type of rock that contains calcium carbonate. Some gravestones are made out of marble. Over time, acid rain wears away the carved lettering on the graves.

(a) Name the process of acid rain wearing away rock.

.... (1)

(b) There is more damage to gravestones caused by acid rain in large cities compared to small villages. Suggest a reason for this.

....

.... (1)

/ 7

Energy Stores and Energy Transfers

Q1 In each of the following examples, underline the main energy store that energy is contained in.

(a) A sandwich.

chemical   **kinetic**   **elastic**   **nuclear**   (1)

(b) A stretched rubber band.

elastic   **nuclear**   **kinetic**   **chemical**   (1)

(c) An atomic nucleus.

chemical   **gravitational potential**   **elastic**   **nuclear**   (1)

Q2 State by which pathway energy is transferred in each of the following examples.

(a) When a falling ball transfers energy from its gravitational potential energy store to its kinetic energy store.

........*Mechanically*.. (1)

(b) When ice cubes are held next to a radiator, energy is transferred from the internal energy store of the radiator to the internal energy store of the ice cubes.

.................*Heating*.. (1)

Q3 A pulley is used to lift a piano to the first floor of a building.

(a) Name the energy store that energy is transferred to as the piano is lifted.

............*Gravitational*.. (1)

(b) The piano is accidentally dropped and falls to the ground.
State the energy store that energy is transferred to when the piano falls.

...........*Kinetic*.. (1)

(c) Suggest by which pathway energy is transferred when the piano hits the ground.

..........*Mechanically*.. (1)

Q4 Louis is investigating the time it takes for a cup of tea to reach room temperature. He pours some boiling water into a cup with a tea bag and holds the cup of tea.

a) Complete the following paragraph, using any of the words in the box below. The words may be used once, more than once or not at all.

increases	chemical	stays the same	gravitational potential
decreases	internal	cool down	elastic	warm up	kinetic

Energy is transferred from the .... energy store of the cup

of tea to the .... energy store of Louis' hand. Whilst this is

happening, the cup of tea will .... and Louis' hand will

.... The temperature difference between the cup of tea

and Louis' hand .... over time. (5)

Louis used a thermometer to measure the tea's temperature at regular intervals after it had been made. The results are presented on the scatter graph below.

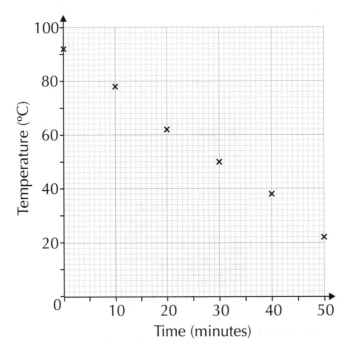

(b) Draw a line of best fit onto the graph above. (1)

(c) Estimate the temperature of the tea after 14 minutes.

.... (1)

/ 15

Section P1 — Energy Transfers and Resources

Conservation of Energy

Q1 Write true or false next to each of these statements about the conservation of energy.

(a) Energy can be destroyed. .... (1)

(b) Energy is only useful when it is transferred
from one store to a useful store. .... (1)

Q2 The diagram shows the amount of energy given out by a television in five minutes.

Input energy →

Useful energy output
= 20 400 J

Wasted energy = 3600 J

Underline the input energy that the television is supplied with in five minutes.

7200 J   **19 200 J**   **20 400 J**   **24 000 J**   (1)

Q3 Charlotte knows that if she rubs her hands together then they warm up.
She says that this happens because energy has been created.

Explain why Charlotte is incorrect.

....

.... (1)

Q4 A car moves by transferring energy from the chemical energy
store of its petrol to a useful energy store.

(a) Name this useful energy store.

.... (1)

(b) Describe how energy is wasted during this transfer between the energy stores.

.... (1)

(c) 60 J of energy in the car battery is supplied to light one of the car's bulbs.
Only 20 J of this energy is used to light the bulb.
Calculate how much energy is wasted.

Energy wasted = ... J (1)

/ 7

Fossil Fuels and Energy Resources

Q1 The following chain shows how energy from the Sun is transferred to food.
Underline the word that correctly fills the gap in the chain.

Sun ⟶ Sun's energy ⟶ .... ⟶ photosynthesis ⟶ food

plants　　　　　**animals**　　　　　**fossil fuels**　　　　　**dead plants**　　　(1)

Q2 Fossil fuels are currently the main energy resources used by humans.

(a)　Name three fossil fuels.

.... (1)

(b)　Use the words and phrases given to fill in the gaps in the passage below
to explain how fossil fuels are formed. You don't have to use all the words
and phrases, but each word or phrase can only be used once.

a few months	**reflect**	**fossil fuels**	**take in**
photosynthesis	**stored**	**millions of years**	
Sun	**respiration**	**destroyed**	**biomass**

Energy from the .... is absorbed by plants during

.... Creatures can .... this energy by

eating the plants. Some of this energy is .... in the tissues of

both the plants and animals. When plants and animals die they can become buried

and slowly decay, and over .... the pressure can

turn these remains into .... (6)

(c)　State how energy can be released from fossil fuels.

.... (1)

/ 9

Generating Electricity and More on Fossil Fuels

Q1 Power stations burn coal to generate electricity.
The diagram below illustrates the process that takes place.

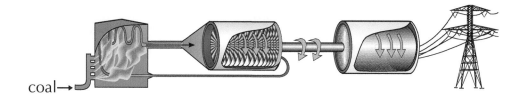

coal→

Describe how coal can be used to generate electricity.
Mention the energy transfer that takes place at the turbine in your answer.

....

....

....

....

....

....

....

.... (4)

Q2 Fossil fuels have other uses apart from generating electricity. For each type of
fossil fuel listed below, give one other use other than the generation of electricity.

(a) Coal

.... (1)

(b) Oil

.... (1)

(c) Natural gas

.... (1)

/ 7

More on Generating Electricity

Q1 Underline the option that completes the sentence below.

Electricity is generated from wave power by...

...waves pushing air in and out of a turbine.

...water continuously flowing through a turbine.

...waves pushing air in and out of a generator.

...water continuously flowing through a generator.

(1)

Q2 Biomass is an example of an energy resource that relies on plants using photosynthesis to capture and store the Sun's energy.

(a) Give one example of biomass.

.... (1)

(b) Name two energy resources that do not rely on photosynthesis.

1. ....

2. .... (2)

Q3 The diagram below outlines how electricity can be generated using geothermal energy.

Describe what is represented by the arrows labelled *x* and *y*.

....

....

.... (2)

/ 6

Section P1 — Energy Transfers and Resources

Renewable and Non-Renewable Energy Resources

Q1 Energy resources can be described as either renewable or non-renewable.

(a) Describe the difference between renewable and non-renewable energy resources.

....

.... (1)

(b) Give two examples of a non-renewable energy resource.

1. ....

2. .... (2)

(c) Give three examples of a renewable energy resource.

1. ....

2. ....

3. .... (3)

Q2 Sophie lives in a country where coal is the most used energy resource. Sophie suggests the government should build solar panels in her town to increase the amount of renewable energy resources used by the country.

(a) Describe two advantages of Sophie's suggestion.

....

....

....

....

.... (2)

(b) Describe two disadvantages of Sophie's suggestion.

....

....

....

....

.... (2)

/ 10

Section P1 — Energy Transfers and Resources

Speed

Q1   An aeroplane flies a total distance of 6600 miles when flying from London to Tokyo.
The flight lasts 12 hours. Calculate the average speed of the aeroplane.

Speed = ... mph   (2)

Q2   Chris and Jenny went to the same beach, but they got there in different ways.

(a)   Jenny took 1000 s to reach the beach and walked 900 m to get there.
Calculate the speed she was travelling at in m/s.

Speed = ... m/s   (2)

(b)   Chris drove 10 km to the beach at a speed of 40 km/h.
Calculate how long it took him to get to the beach in hours.

Time = ... hours   (2)

Q3   A scientist is investigating the properties of various liquids. He drops
a metal ball down a tube filled with one of the liquids and measures
how long it takes for the ball to pass between two marks on the tube.
The marks are 50 cm apart. The table below shows some of his results.

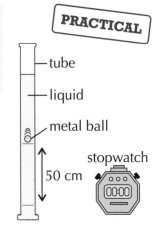

PRACTICAL

Liquid	Time for ball to pass between marks (s)	Speed (m/s)
A	5	
B		2.5
C	2	0.25

(a)   Calculate the speed of the ball in liquid A in metres per second.

Speed = ... m/s   (3)

(b)   Calculate how many seconds the ball took to pass between the marks in liquid B.

Time = ... s   (2)

/ 11

More on Speed

Q1 A car is overtaking a bus on a motorway.

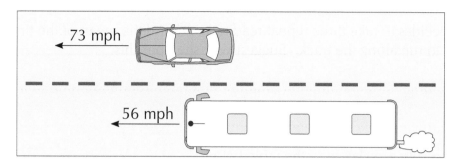

Calculate the speed of the car relative to the bus.

Speed = ... mph (1)

Q2 The diagram below shows two trains that are moving towards each other on separate tracks.

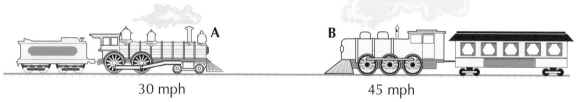

30 mph   45 mph

Calculate the speed of train B relative to train A.

Speed = ... mph (1)

Q3 A horse trainer wants to compare the speeds of two different horses.

(a) Describe a method she can use to calculate the speed of
each horse as it runs round a 1 km race track.

....

....

.... (2)

(b) Describe how the trainer can make sure her results are repeatable.

....

.... (1)

(c) Give one way that the trainer can make sure the investigation is a fair test.

....

.... (1)

Q4 Anna is part of her school's running team. She wants to calculate the speed of each of her teammates as they run along a track.

PRACTICAL

(a) State one piece of equipment she will need.

.... (1)

(b) Anna decides to take three repeat readings and find the mean of the time it takes each runner to run along the track. Suggest why she does this.

....

.... (1)

Some of her results are shown in the table below.

Runner	Time (s)			
	Measurement 1	Measurement 2	Measurement 3	Mean
1	12.0	11.0	11.5	11.5
2	13.0	12.5	12.0	12.5
3	11.5	12.0	21.5	15.0
4	12.5	13.5	13.0	13.0

(c) State the fastest runner.

.... (1)

(d) The total distance along the track is 100 m.
Calculate the mean speed of Runner 2.

Speed = ... m/s (2)

(e) One of the runner's measurements was affected by a random error.
(i) Identify this runner.

.... (1)

(ii) Anna repeats this measurement and gets a new time of 12.5 s.
Recalculate the runner's mean time.

Mean time = ... s (1)

/ 13

Section P2 — Speed and Forces

Stopping Distances

Q1 The stopping distance of a vehicle is the sum of the thinking distance and the braking distance. Anything that reduces friction between the tyres and the road will increase the braking distance.

(a) Underline the factor below that would be the most likely to increase braking distance.

a dry road

a rough road

a wet road

tyres with a deep tread (1)

The diagram below shows some information about the distance it takes a car to brake.

Thinking distance   Braking distance

16 m

(b) The stopping distance of the car is 74 m.
Calculate the car's braking distance.

Braking distance = ... m   (2)

An engineer conducts an experiment to investigate the effect of speed on stopping distance. Three identical cars are driven around a race track at different speeds. The drivers are instructed to brake as soon as they hear a signal. The results are shown in the table below.

Car	Stopping distance (m)
A	36
B	96
C	23

(c) Suggest which car was travelling the fastest. Explain your answer.

....

.... (2)

(d) Suggest two factors, other than the cars used, their speed and the road surface, that could affect stopping distance.

1. ....

2. .... (2)

/ 7

Forces

Q1 Forces can't be seen, but their effects can be.

(a) State what is meant by a force.

.... (1)

(b) Complete the sentence.

Forces are measured in units called .... (1)

(c) Applying a force to an object can cause it to speed up or start moving. State two other effects that applying a force can have on an object.

1. ....

2. .... (2)

(d) Force diagrams are used to show the forces acting on an object. Describe which two pieces of information about the forces acting on an object are shown by an arrow.

....

.... (2)

Q2 The parachute on a drag racing car travelling at a steady speed opens, causing a drag force to act in the opposite direction to the car's motion. Write down the main effect of this force on the movement of the car.

.... (1)

Q3 The diagram below shows a car driving along a road. The arrow shows the force from the engine. The friction acting on the car is equal to the force from the engine. Draw a second arrow onto the diagram to show the friction acting on the car.

force from engine

(2)

/ 9

Balanced and Unbalanced Forces

Q1 Write down the letter of all the force diagrams below which show balanced forces.

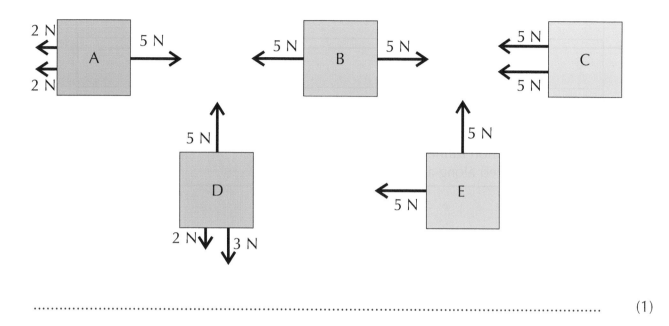

.... (1)

Q2 For each sentence below, underline the option that best completes it.

(a) The diagram below shows the forces acting on a shark.

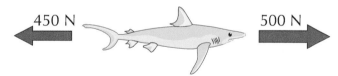

The shark is

speeding up   slowing down   travelling at constant speed   at rest (1)

(b) The diagram below shows the forces acting on a helicopter.

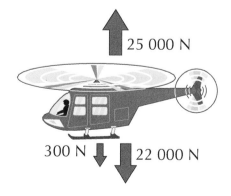

The helicopter is

moving upwards at   moving downwards at   moving upwards at
an increasing speed   an increasing speed   a constant speed   at rest (1)

Q3 For the scenarios in the table below, put a tick or a cross in the final two columns to show whether the forces involved are balanced or unbalanced.

Scenario	Balanced	Unbalanced
A cyclist starting off.		
A car slowing down.		
A model trolley travelling down a slope.		
A marathon runner going at a steady speed along a straight road.		

(2)

Q4 A cherry is placed on a cake. There are two forces acting on the cherry — an upward force from the cake's frosting and the downward force of the cherry's weight.

(a) State what will happen to the cherry if the two forces are balanced.

.... (1)

(b) State what will happen to the cherry if its weight is larger than the force from the frosting.

.... (1)

Q5 A car is travelling forwards along a road.

The diagram below shows the horizontal forces acting on the car.

7000 N

1000 N

6000 N

(a) Explain whether the forces acting on the car are balanced or unbalanced.

....

.... (1)

(b) The driver increases the driving force until the forces on the car are balanced. Describe the motion of the car when the forces are balanced.

.... (1)

/ 9

Section P2 — Speed and Forces

Friction and Air Resistance

Q1 An ice skater skates across an ice rink.

(a) State what is meant by friction.

....

.... (1)

(b) Friction acts between the ice skates and the ice.
(i) Describe one way in which this friction is an advantage when skating.

....

.... (1)

(ii) Describe one way in which this friction is a disadvantage when skating.

....

.... (1)

Q2 A skydiver falling through the air has opposing forces acting on her due to gravity and air resistance.

(a) State what is meant by air resistance.

....

.... (1)

(b) Explain why the skydiver starts to fall rapidly when she first steps out of the plane.

....

.... (1)

(c) (i) State what happens to air resistance when the skydiver's parachute opens.

.... (1)

(ii) Explain why the skydiver falls at a steady speed with the parachute open.

....

.... (1)

Q3 Aroosa makes a small parachute for a weight by suspending the weight from a square of thin plastic material with some thread.

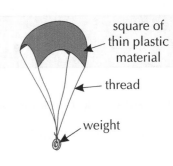

square of
thin plastic
material

thread

weight

(a) Aroosa wants to find out how the area of the parachute's canopy affects the air resistance it provides to the weight when it is dropped. Describe a method Aroosa could use to investigate this, including what she should do and what measurements she should take.

....

....

....

....

....

....

....

....

.... **(4)**

(b) State two variables that should be controlled.

....

.... **(2)**

(c) Explain why Aroosa should repeat any measurements she carries out.

.... **(1)**

(d) Suggest the purpose of suspending a weight from the parachute instead of simply dropping each parachute by itself.

....

.... **(1)**

(e) Suggest what the results from this experiment will show. Explain your answer.

....

....

.... **(2)**

/ 17

Section P2 — Speed and Forces

Springs

Q1 Manny is placing blocks of different weights on top of a spring and measuring the spring's compression.

(a) Describe how Manny would measure the spring's compression.

....

....

.... (2)

(b) (i) State the independent variable in this experiment.

.... (1)

(ii) State the dependent variable in this experiment.

.... (1)

Manny's results are shown below. The table is incomplete.

Weight (N)	Compression (cm)			
	Reading 1	**Reading 2**	**Reading 3**	**Mean**
0.1	0.9	1.0	0.8	0.9
0.2	1.9	1.9	1.8	1.9
0.3	2.7	2.3	2.5	2.5
0.4	3.6	3.9	3.6	

(c) Calculate the mean compression of the spring when the 0.4 N weight was added.

Mean = ... cm (1)

(d) State which weight has the most precise results. Explain your answer.

....

.... (2)

(e) Write a conclusion for the experiment.

....

.... (1)

/ 8

Pressure

Q1 Complete the sentences below by underlining the correct option.

Pressure is calculated using **force divided by area** / **area divided by force** .

The greater the area over which the force acts, the **smaller** / **greater** the pressure.   (1)

Q2 Anne sees a pencil lying on her desk. The pencil has a weight of 0.20 N. She manages to balance it on its end.

(a) Each side of the pencil has an area of 2.5 cm². Calculate the pressure exerted by the pencil on the desk when it is lying on its side.

Pressure = ... N/cm²   (2)

(b) When the pencil is balanced on its end, it exerts a pressure of 0.4 N/cm² on the desk. Calculate the area of the pencil's end.

Area = ... cm²   (2)

Q3 The diagram shows a pair of traditional snowshoes. They are designed to have a large area. In snowy weather, one is attached to the bottom of each shoe to make walking easier. Explain how this works.

....

....

....

....

....   (3)

Q4 A student drama company is designing a small wooden walkway that is able to support one person. They need to make sure the wood is thick enough to withstand the pressure of someone standing in the centre of it.

Students cut identical lengths of wood of different thicknesses. They support the length at each end and place three bags of sand in the centre. The total weight of the sand is 600 N, which is about the average weight of a human. They record whether or not the wood bends or breaks under the weight.

(a) State the independent variable in this test.

.... (1)

(b) Describe how the students can calculate the pressure exerted on the wood by the bags of sand.

....

.... (1)

(c) Suggest why the students used bags of sand rather than a person to test the wood.

.... (1)

(d) Explain why this method could lead to them using a wood thickness that is too weak to hold a human who weighs 600 N.

....

....

.... (2)

Q5 The diagram on the right shows a balloon that has been dropped onto a bed of nails. When the same balloon is dropped onto a single nail, it pops.

Explain why the balloon pops on a single nail but not on the bed of nails.

....

....

....

....

.... (3)

/ 16

Density

Q1 Xiomara has a cuboid-shaped pendant with rounded edges as shown in the diagram. It is made from glass with a density of 2.5 g/cm³.

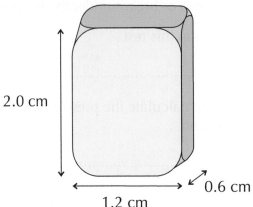

2.0 cm

1.2 cm

0.6 cm

(a) State the relationship between density, volume and mass.

.... (1)

(b) (i) Estimate the volume of the pendant.

Volume = ... cm³ (1)

(ii) Use your answer from part (b) (i) to estimate the mass of the pendant.

Mass = ... g (2)

(c) She uses a mass balance to find the mass of the pendant.
Explain whether the mass will be higher or lower than your estimate.

....

.... (1)

(d) Describe how Xiomara could use a measuring cylinder and a jug of water to get a more accurate value for the volume of the pendant.

....

....

....

.... (3)

Q2 Michael is given a container filled with an unknown liquid by his teacher. He is asked to find the density of the liquid. Describe how Michael can find the density of the liquid using a measuring beaker and mass balance.

....

....

....

....

....

.... (4)

Q3 Gary has an antique spoon. He wants to find out whether it is made from a valuable metal.

He places the spoon into a measuring beaker filled with water.
Before inserting the spoon, he notes that the water has a volume of 250.0 cm³.
When the spoon is completely submerged in the beaker, the water level rises to 255.0 cm³.

(a) Calculate the volume of the spoon.

Volume = ... cm³ (1)

He looks up the densities of different metals and finds the table below.

Metal	Density / g/cm³
Gold	19.3
Copper	8.9
Brass	8.4 – 8.7

(b) He measures the mass of the spoon to be 45 g.
Suggest whether the spoon is most likely to be made from gold, copper or brass. Explain your answer.

....

....

....

.... (2)

/ 15

PRACTICAL

More on Density

Q1 Tamsin is doing an experiment to investigate density. She chooses two immiscible liquids, oil and water, and adds equal amounts of them to a beaker. She watches as the liquids form two layers.

(a) Underline the option below that correctly defines 'immiscible liquids'.

Liquids that chemically react together.   **Liquids that have the same density.**

Liquids that don't mix together.   **Liquids that have different colours.** (1)

(b) Describe how Tamsin's experiment can be used to investigate density.

....

.... (1)

Q2 Sabaa adds dark green food colouring to a beaker of warm water and light green food colouring to a beaker of cold water. She then carefully pours some of the coloured warm water into the beaker of coloured cold water and waits a few seconds.

Which of the diagrams on the right do you think represents Sabaa's results? Explain your answer in terms of the arrangement of water particles.

A   B   C

Beaker: .... Explanation: ....

....

....

.... (3)

Q3 You can measure the mass and volume of a gas to find its density.

Describe a method you could use to estimate the density of air using a balloon.

....

....

....

....

....

.... (4)

/ 9

Sound

Q1 Complete the paragraph using words from the box below.

vibrating	**solids**	**medium**
vacuum	**finite**	**particles**

A sound wave is a wave of vibrating .... which are produced

by a .... object. In order to travel, sound waves require a

.... Whilst sound can't travel through a .... it can

travel through ...., liquids and air. In different mediums sound

has a .... speed.

(6)

Q2 While sitting at home, Russell hears an explosion from a nearby quarry.

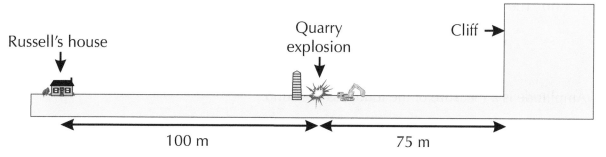

(a) Just before he heard the explosion, he felt a faint vibration in the ground.
Explain why he felt vibrations in the ground before he heard the explosion.

....

....

.... (2)

(b) 0.71 seconds after he heard the explosion, he heard an echo.
Calculate the speed of sound of the explosion using the formula:
speed = distance ÷ time. Show your working.

Speed = ... m/s (2)

/ 10

More on Sound

Q1 Four traces of sound waves with different frequencies are shown below.

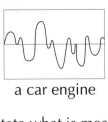
a car engine

a scream

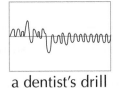
a dentist's drill

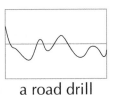
a road drill

(a) (i) State what is meant by the frequency of a wave.

.... (1)

(ii) Describe the relationship between the frequency of a noise
and the way it sounds.

.... (1)

(b) Complete each of the following sentences by underlining the correct option.
(i) The noise with the lowest frequency is the

car engine   **scream**   **dentist's drill**   **road drill**   (1)

(ii) The noise with the loudest sound is the

car engine   **scream**   **dentist's drill**   **road drill**   (1)

Q2 Amplitude is a measure of the loudness of sound.

(a) State whether each of the following statements is true or false.

(i) The amplitude shows how much energy the sound has.   .... (1)

(ii) A large amplitude means the wave has little energy.   .... (1)

(iii) A cat's meow has a smaller amplitude than a lion's roar.   .... (1)

(b) An oscilloscope can be used to display sound waves. Describe how you can
determine the amplitude of a sound wave from an oscilloscope.

.... (1)

(c) Earplugs are designed to reduce the loudness of any noise that the user is
exposed to. Explain why a musician may be advised to wear earplugs at
their concerts.

.... (1)

/ 9

Hearing

Q1 The table shows the auditory range of a selection of animals.

Animal	Lowest frequency (Hz)	Highest frequency (Hz)
Human	20	20 000
Cat	50	80 000
Shark	10	800
Pigeon	1	10 000

a) State what is meant by auditory range.

....

.... (1)

b) State the animal from the table being described by each sentence.

    i) It can hear the highest pitched sounds.   .... (1)

    ii) It has the smallest auditory range.   .... (1)

Q2 Matthew is carrying out an experiment to find the highest frequency of sound that his family members can hear. He sets up a speaker that can play sounds of different frequencies. Each family member being tested sits with their back to the speaker and raises their hand every time they hear a sound from it. **PRACTICAL**

(a) Briefly describe what Matthew could do to find the highest frequency sound each family member can hear.

....

....

....

.... (2)

(b) Give two things that should be kept the same for each person to make it a fair test.

1. ....

2. .... (2)

(c) Matthew tested his grandparents, his parents and his younger brother and sister. Suggest and explain who was least likely to hear the high frequency sounds.

....

.... (2)

/ 9

Light

Q1 Miranda used a pinhole camera to look at an eagle.

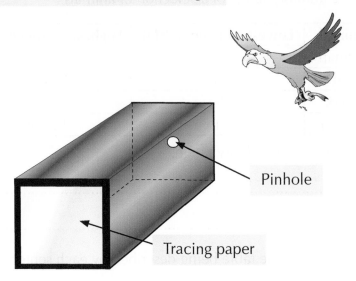

(a) Complete the sentence below by underlining the best option.

The pinhole needs to be small so that...

...only one ray from each point on the object gets into the camera.

...the inside of the box is kept very dark.

...the lens doesn't have to be big.

...you can only look at the image with one eye.

(1)

(b) (i) Draw two light rays on the diagram of a pinhole camera below to show how the image of this object is formed.

(2)

(ii) Use the diagram you have drawn to explain how an image viewed through a pinhole camera would differ from the object observed.

....

....

....

(2)

Q2 Underline the option that completes the following sentences about light waves.

(a) Light waves travel...

...more slowly than sound waves.

...more quickly when they have to travel through matter.

...in a straight line. (1)

(b) Light waves travel fastest in a

liquid **vacuum** **solid** (1)

Q3 Jacques is investigating the speed of sound in a lab. A speaker is placed 30 metres away from a sensor. The speaker produces a short pulse of sound that is detected by the sensor. The sensor measures time since the pulse was produced to the nearest hundredth of a second. Jacques writes down how long it took the sound pulse to reach the sensor and uses this to calculate its speed.

[PRACTICAL]

(a) Jacques wants to measure the speed of light. He decides to do the same experiment, but replace the speaker with a light source and change the settings of the sensor so that it detects light instead of sound. Suggest why this experiment will not work.

....

....

....

.... (2)

(b) Jacques carries out another experiment. His friend fires a starting pistol from the other side of a large field. Predict and explain whether Jacques would hear the gun before, after or at the same time as seeing it fire.

Prediction: ....

Explanation: .... (1)

(c) Explain why light waves can travel through a vacuum but sound waves cannot. You should use the word particles in your answer.

....

....

....

.... (2)

/ 12

Reflection

Q1 Mirrors are able to reflect light.

(a) A periscope uses mirrors to allow the user to see over obstacles. Add a ray to the diagram on the right to show how the light from the object reaches the user's eye.

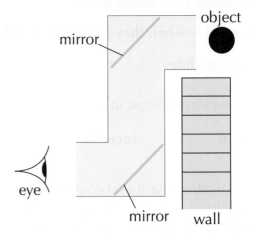

(2)

(b) Traditional cameras use mirrors so that light entering through the lens is reflected out of the viewfinder to the eye of the photographer. The photo and diagram below show light entering and leaving a camera. Complete the diagram to show how light is reflected through the camera.

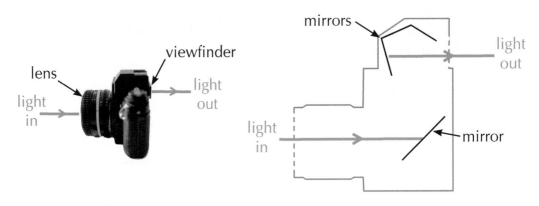

(2)

Q2 A falcon sees a prairie dog ahead of it.

A puddle in front of the prairie dog acts as a plane mirror.
Explain whether or not the prairie dog is able to see the falcon's reflection.

....

....

.... (2)

/ 6

Refraction

Q1 A diver uses a torch underwater. The light is visible above the water's surface. Water is denser than air.

(a) Complete the sentence below.

When the light passes from the water to the air at an angle to the normal

it changes .... This is known as ....   (1)

(b) Underline the correct word(s) to complete the sentence below.

As the light travels from a more dense medium to a less dense medium,

it bends   **towards**   the normal.
         away from   (1)

(c) Complete the diagrams below to show what happens to light when it moves between media.

(i)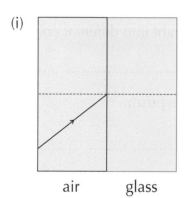

air   glass

(ii)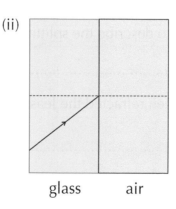

glass   air

(iii)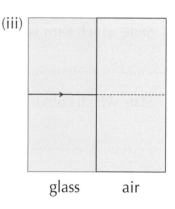

glass   air   (3)

(d) Complete the diagram below to show what happens when light travels from air to water, and then into glass.

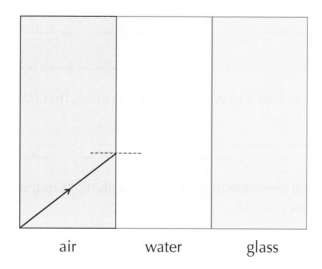

air   water   glass

(2)

/ 7

Light and Materials

Q1 When white light passes through a glass prism it bends and is split up into different colours. A range of colours appears on the screen.

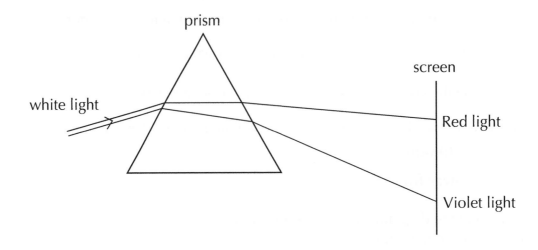

(a) State which term is used to describe the splitting of light into different colours.

.... (1)

(b) State which colour has been refracted the least by the prism.

.... (1)

(c) Explain why white light splits up into different colours when passed through a prism.

....

....

....

.... (3)

(d) State the name given to a material, such as a prism, that transmits light rather than absorbing it.

.... (1)

(e) Describe a natural phenomenon in which white light naturally splits into different colours.

....

.... (2)

/ 8

Electrical Circuits

Q1 The diagram below shows a simple circuit, containing a cell and a bulb.

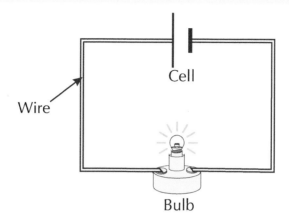

(a) Underline the correct words to complete the sentences below.

The more cells there are in a circuit, the **higher** / **lower** the current.

Current **is** / **is not** used up as it flows around a circuit.

(2)

(b) Explain what would happen to the bulb if one of the wires were to be replaced by an insulating material.

....

.... (2)

Q2 Three materials were put, one at a time, in an electrical circuit with a battery. The current in each material was measured and is shown in the table below.

The resistance of Material B is also shown in the table.
The other two materials have a resistance of 0.00 Ω and 1.06 Ω.
Complete the table below, filling in the correct resistance for Material A and C.
Use the results to state whether each material is more likely to be a conductor or an insulator.

Material	Current (A)	Resistance (Ω)	Conductor or insulator?
A	0.00024	....	....
B	16	0.03	conductor
C	10	....	....

(4)

More on Electrical Circuits

Q1 Underline the option that completes the sentences below.

(a)   The component above is

a reed switch   **a push-button switch**   **a relay**   **an SPST**   (1)

(b)   A resistor...

... spins when a current passes through it

... lights up when a current passes through it

... is controlled by a magnetic field

... reduces current   (1)

(c)   A variable resistor...

... decreases the resistance when light is shone on it

... is a switch controlled by a magnetic field

... gives control over reduction in current

... measures current   (1)

Q2 A circuit containing a battery, a bulb and a buzzer is shown below.

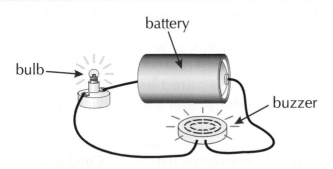

Draw an accurate circuit diagram of this circuit in the space below.

(3)

Q3 The diagram shows a cell connected to a component.

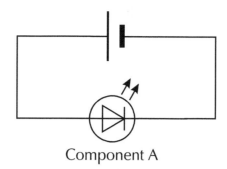

Component A

(a) State the name of component A.

.... (1)

(b) (i) Give the units of current.

.... (1)

   (ii) State the name of the component used to measure current.

.... (1)

(c) More cells are added to the circuit above, which causes the
current to increase. This may cause damage to component A.
Suggest one additional component that should be added to
protect component A from high currents.

.... (1)

Q4 A student puts together a circuit consisting of a battery, a light dependent
resistor and a motor. She wants to test how the speed of the motor is affected
by the intensity of the light shone on the light dependent resistor.

(a) Complete the circuit diagram below to show the circuit described.

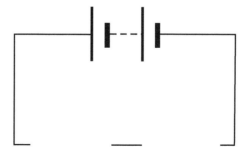

(2)

(b) State the independent variable in the student's experiment.

.... (1)

/ 13

Series Circuits

Q1 Ammeter A₁ in the circuit below reads 2 A.

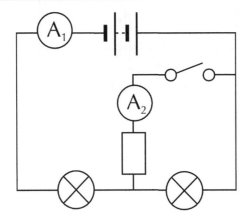

(a) Explain how you can tell from the diagram that the bulbs are in series.

....

.... (1)

(b) State the current recorded at ammeter A₂, and explain your answer.

....

.... (1)

(c) State what will happen to the current if a third cell is added into the circuit.

.... (1)

Q2 A student sets up the circuit shown below.

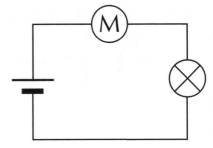

The student removes the motor, then reconnects the rest of the circuit.
Underline the correct words to complete the sentences.

Removing the motor from the circuit will **increase / decrease / not affect** the

resistance in the circuit. This will **increase / decrease / not affect** the current flowing.

The current measured will be **the same / different** at any point in the circuit. (3)

/ 6

Section P5 — Circuits and Magnets

Parallel Circuits

Q1 The circuit on the right has three bulbs, 1-3.

(a) State which of the three bulbs would be lit if only switch A was open.

.... (1)

(b) State which of the three bulbs would be lit if only switch B was open.

.... (1)

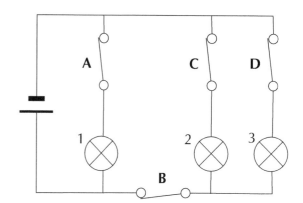

Q2 Components in parallel circuits are connected on separate loops of wire.

The diagram below shows a parallel circuit that contains a cell, two bulbs, a motor and five ammeters.

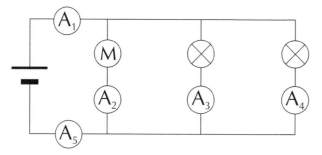

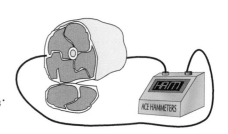

The table below shows the readings for ammeters A_1, A_2 and A_3. Complete the table to show all the ammeter readings.

Ammeter	A_1	A_2	A_3	A_4	A_5
Reading (A)	9.2	3.9	2.6		

(2)

Q3 In the space below, draw a circuit diagram of a simple battery-powered circuit that allows a bulb and a buzzer to be switched on and off independently of each other.

(4)

/ 8

Magnets

Q1 A bar magnet has a magnetic field.

(a) Draw the field lines around the bar magnet below to illustrate its magnetic field.

| N | S |

(2)

(b) Describe how field lines illustrate the strength of a magnetic field at a given point.

....

.... (1)

(c) Describe how to use a plotting compass to find the shape of a bar magnet's magnetic field.

....

.... (1)

Q2 Bertie is given two grey blocks, block 1 and block 2, by his teacher.

He holds the end of block 1 up to the end of block 2 and finds that they attract each other.

Bertie concludes that either one or both of the blocks is a magnet.
Bertie flips block 2 around and finds that they still attract each other.

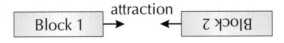

(a) State what Bertie's conclusion should now be.

.... (1)

(b) Explain how Bertie could find out for sure whether each block is a magnet or not.

....

.... (2)

Q3 Astrid decides to compare the strengths of five different magnets. To do this, one at a time she places each magnet and a paperclip on a surface and moves the paperclip towards the magnet beside a ruler. She measures the distance at which she first feels the pull of the magnet on the paperclip.

PRACTICAL

(a) State one variable that should remain constant in this experiment.

.... (1)

(b) Astrid realises that she has lined up the end of the magnet with the end of the ruler instead of the zero. State what type of error this is.

.... (1)

Astrid records her results in the table below.

Magnet	1	2	3	4	5
Distance (cm)	4.2	0.6	3.1	2.8	2.7

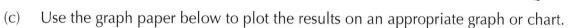

(c) Use the graph paper below to plot the results on an appropriate graph or chart.

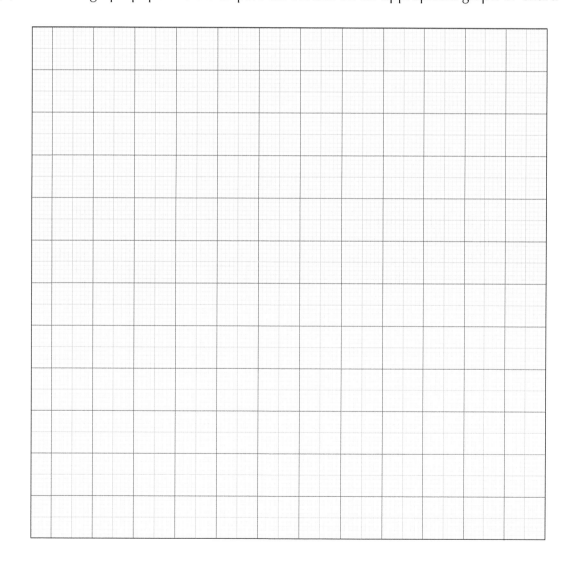

(4)

/ 13

Electromagnets

Q1 Electromagnets have many useful applications.

(a) Describe how an electromagnet could be constructed from a piece of insulated wire and an iron bar.

....

.... (2)

(b) State the main difference between this type of magnet and a bar magnet.

....

.... (1)

(c) Suggest two ways of increasing the strength of an electromagnet.

1. ....

2. .... (2)

(d) Explain how iron filings can be used to test for the magnetic field of an electromagnet.

....

.... (1)

Q2 The diagram on the right shows a simple relay circuit. The input circuit contains a switch that connects it to a power supply when it is closed.

(a) Explain how a relay circuit works.

....

....

....

....

.... (3)

(b) Name one other practical use of electromagnets.

.... (1)

/ 10

Gravity

Q1 Quentin is using a newton meter to measure the weight of a metal disc on Earth.
The newton meter and metal disc are shown below.

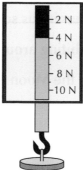

(a) Describe what causes the disc to have a weight on Earth.

....

.... (1)

(b) Complete the following equation to show how to calculate weight.

weight = ... (1)

(c) The gravitational field strength on Earth is 10 N/kg.
Using this information and the diagram above, calculate the mass of the disc.

Mass = ... kg (3)

(d) Calculate the weight of the disc if it were measured on Mars.
The gravitational field strength on Mars is 3.7 N/kg.

Weight = ... N (2)

Q2 An astronaut has a weight of 128 N and a mass of 80 kg on the Moon.

Calculate the Moon's gravitational field strength.

Mass = ... N/kg (2)

/ 9

The Solar System

Q1 Underline the statement below that is true about the Moon.

The Moon is the closest planet to Earth.

We can see the Moon because it is a luminous source.

The Earth's gravity keeps the Moon orbiting around the Earth.

A year represents the time it takes for the Moon to fully orbit the Earth. (1)

Q2 Our Solar System is made up of the Sun and the things that orbit around it, such as planets.

(a) Astronomers have discovered over 3000 stars in the Milky Way galaxy that have planets orbiting them. These are called planetary systems.

The nearest star to our Solar System is called Proxima Centauri. Astronomers have confirmed that it has two planets moving in orbit around it.

Give one similarity and one difference between the Proxima Centauri planetary system and our Solar System.

Similarity: ....

Difference: .... (2)

(b) Describe what keeps the planets in orbit around the Sun.

....

.... (2)

(c) (i) State the orbital period of the Earth around the Sun.

.... (1)

(ii) Which of these planets would you expect to have the longest orbital period: Venus, Saturn or Uranus? Explain your answer.

....

.... (2)

(d) Apart from planets, name one other type of object in space that moves in an orbit, and state what it orbits around.

.... (1)

/ 9

Section P6 — Space

The Movement of the Earth

Q1 The Sun and stars appear to move across the sky over time.

(a) Explain why the Sun appears to move across the sky over the course of a day.

....

.... (1)

(b) At night-time, a star known as the Pole Star appears to remain stationary.
The rest of the stars appear to follow a circular path around the Pole Star.

Explain why all of the stars appear to move, and suggest why the Pole Star doesn't.

....

....

.... (2)

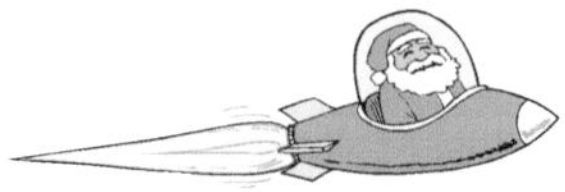

Q2 A total lunar eclipse could be seen from the UK on 21st January 2019,
whilst a total solar eclipse could be seen from the UK on 11th August 1999.

(a) Describe the difference between a total solar eclipse and a partial solar eclipse.

....

.... (1)

(b) (i) On the diagram below, draw the relative position of the Sun
that would result in a lunar eclipse on Earth.
The diagram has not been drawn to scale.

Earth   ● Moon

(1)

(ii) Explain why the Moon is less visible during a lunar eclipse.

....

....

.... (2)

Q3 The diagram below shows the Earth in its orbit during June.
Use the diagram to answer the following questions.

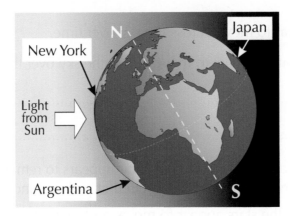

(a) (i) Out of the locations labelled on the diagram,
state where it is currently night-time.

.... (1)

(ii) In 12 hours' time, night will become day at this location.
Explain why this change occurs.

....

....

....

.... (2)

(b) It is summer in New York and winter in Argentina during the month of June.
Explain why it is generally warmer in New York than in Argentina in June.

....

....

....

....

....

.... (3)

(c) Describe how the Sun's path across the sky is different in summer
compared to winter.

....

.... (1)

/ 14

Satellites

Q1 Underline the option that completes the following sentence about probes.

A probe is...

...a natural satellite.

...an object that humans have put into orbit around a planet.

...an unmanned spacecraft.

...a type of telescope. (1)

Q2 Artificial satellites such as the one shown on the right are often put into orbit around the Earth.

(a) Describe one way that satellites like these can be used to help us understand more about the Solar System.

....

....

.... (1)

(b) Suggest one way that artificial satellites like these could help scientists on an expedition to an uninhabited island.

....

.... (1)

Q3 Since the 1960s, many unmanned spacecraft have been sent to fly by, orbit or land on Mars in order to observe it. However, there has yet to be a manned mission to Mars.

(a) Suggest why unmanned spacecraft have been sent to explore Mars instead of manned spacecraft.

....

.... (1)

(b) Suggest what information could be collected with an unmanned spacecraft that would be useful for sending a manned spacecraft to Mars.

....

.... (1)

/ 5

CGP

SURNAME	
FIRST NAME	
JUNIOR SCHOOL	
SENIOR SCHOOL	

CGP practice exam paper for:

COMMON ENTRANCE 13+

SCIENCE

LEVEL 2

BIOLOGY

Fill in your details in the spaces provided above.

Read this information before you start.

- Time allowed: 40 minutes.
- You should attempt **all** of the questions.
- You may use a calculator.

1. For each of the following, underline the option that best completes the sentence.

(7)

(a) Respiration is an important process that

moves gases in and out of the lungs

uses carbon dioxide to make glucose

releases energy from food

increases plant biomass

(b) The female part of a flowering plant includes the

sepal   **anther**   **stamen**   **stigma**

(c) The animal below has smooth moist skin and lays eggs in water.

It is

a mammal   **an amphibian**   **a reptile**   **a bird**

(d) Iodine solution can be used to test for the presence of

starch   **sugar**   **oxygen**   **carbon dioxide**

(e) The rate of photosynthesis may slow down if the amount of

light a plant gets increases

carbon dioxide available decreases

oxygen available increases

chlorophyll in a plant increases

(f) Arthropods are part of the

plant kingdom   **protist kingdom**   **animal kingdom**   **fungi kingdom**

(g) A wind-pollinated plant is likely to have

feathery stigmas   **nectar**   **scented flowers**   **bright petals**

(7)

2. The diagram below shows the female reproductive system.

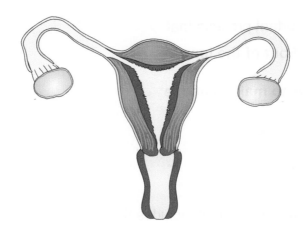

(a) Choose the correct words from the box to complete the following sentences.

an ovary	**the womb**	**the umbilical cord**
the placenta	**the urethra**	**a fallopian tube**

During the menstrual cycle, an egg is released from ....

It then travels along .... to the womb. If the egg has not

been fertilised before it reaches the womb, then the lining of

.... breaks down. (3)

(b) Explain the role of the testes in reproduction.

....

....

.... (2)

(c) Name the part of the female reproductive system where an embryo grows.

.... (1)

3. The image below shows a photograph of a human cell as seen down a light microscope.

    (a) Complete the labels on the photograph.

7.5 cm

....

....

(2)

    (b) Complete the following sentence:

    All of the structures within an animal cell are surrounded by

    a jelly-like substance called ....

(1)

The cell in the photograph is one of a group of similar cells working together.

    (c) State the name given to a group of similar cells.

    .... (1)

The cell appeared to be 7.5 cm long when viewed under the microscope.
The magnification used to view the cell was × 1500.

    (d) Calculate the real length of the cell.

    Use the formula: magnification = $\dfrac{\text{image size}}{\text{real size}}$

    Show your working.

    Real length of cell = ... cm (2)

4. The table below shows nutritional details taken from the packets of two different brands of crisps — Brand A and Brand B.

	Energy (J)	Protein (g)	Carbohydrate (g)	Fat (g)	Fibre (g)
Brand A	2 050 000	6.2	56.2	28.7	4.2
Brand B	1 300 000	9.2	45.1	10.5	9.1

(a) Explain why fibre is an important part of a balanced diet.

....

.... (1)

(b) Using the table, state which brand of crisps is the healthier option.
Give a reason for your answer.

Brand: ....

Reason: ....

.... (2)

A student wanted to test the amount of energy in the two brands of crisps.
She used the set-up shown below to heat some water using the crisps' energy.
The energy is released from the crisps by burning them. She measured the
starting and finishing temperatures of the water in the boiling tube.

(c) Write a prediction for this experiment.

....

.... (1)

(d) Suggest two variables the student should have kept the same in the experiment to make it a fair test.

1. ....

2. .... (2)

(e) Give one safety precaution that the student should have followed.

.... (1)

The student's results are shown in the table below.

Brand	Starting temperature (°C)	Finishing temperature (°C)	Temperature change (°C)
A	22	50	....
B	19	43	....

(f) Complete the table above. (1)

(g) State how the student could improve the reliability of her results.

.... (1)

A lot of heat was lost to the surroundings during the experiment.

(h) Suggest one change that the student could make to the apparatus to reduce this heat loss.

.... (1)

5. A food web from a garden ecosystem is shown below.

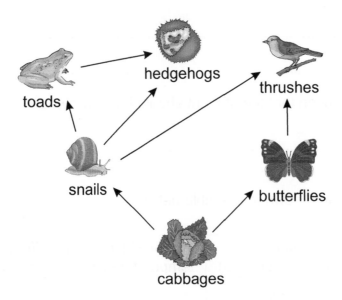

A gardener notices one year that the number of snails in his garden has decreased.

(a) Suggest an explanation for each of the following consequences.

   (i)   The population of thrushes decreases.

   .... (1)

   (ii)   The population of butterflies increases.

   .... (1)

(b) Suggest how the toad population might have changed in the garden as a
     consequence of the decrease in snail numbers. Explain your answer.

   ....

   .... (1)

(c) Explain how the thrush and the cabbage are interdependent in this garden ecosystem.

   ....

   ....

   ....

   .... (2)

The gardener wants to investigate how the size of the population of snails in his garden compares to other gardens.

(d) Describe a method that the gardener could use to estimate the number of snails in his garden.

....

....

....

....

....

....

.... (4)

(e) The gardener thinks that a lower soil pH could reduce the number of snails in a garden. He measures the average pH of the soil and the average number of snails in the gardens along his street. A graph of his results is shown below.

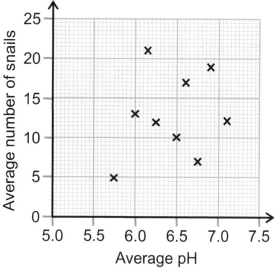

(i) The gardener says "the graph shows that as the pH increases, the number of snails also increases". State whether the gardener is correct. Explain your answer.

....

.... (1)

(ii) Give two ways that the gardener could improve his sampling method.

1. ....

2. .... (2)

6. A scientist set up the following experiment to investigate the effect of light intensity on the rate of photosynthesis. She dissolved some sodium bicarbonate in the water to act as a source of carbon dioxide.

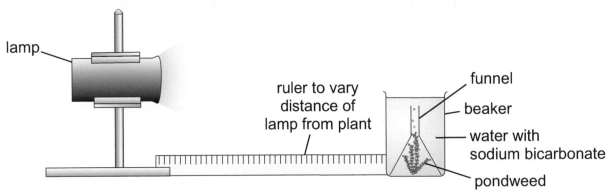

The results of this experiment are shown in the table.

Distance of lamp from beaker (cm)	Number of bubbles produced by the pondweed in 1 minute
100	2
80	5
60	9
40	20
20	39

(a) Plot the results of this experiment on the graph paper below.
    Draw a curve of best fit through the points.

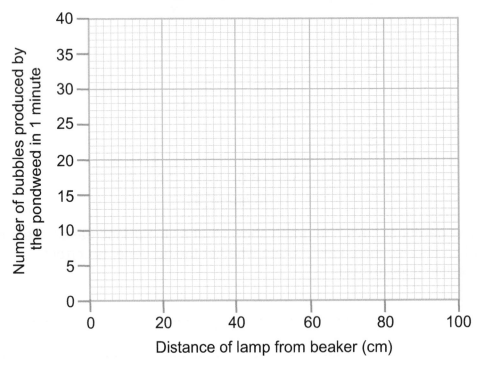

(3)

(b) Write a conclusion for this experiment.

....

.... (1)

(c) Suggest one way that the method for this experiment could be improved.

....

.... (1)

(d) Describe how the scientist could modify the experiment on the previous page to investigate the effect of carbon dioxide concentration on the rate of photosynthesis.

....

.... (1)

7. Respiration is a chemical process. It can be aerobic or anaerobic.

Martha is investigating aerobic respiration in woodlice.
She sets up the apparatus as shown below.

woodlice   limewater

(a) Describe the result that Martha should expect to observe from this experiment.
Explain your answer.

Observation: ....

Explanation: ....

.... (2)

(b) Give one reason why animals respire aerobically when possible,
rather than anaerobically.

....

.... (1)

(c) Complete the word equation for anaerobic respiration in humans.

.... → .... (+ some energy) (1)

(d)   A man jogs for 10 minutes on a treadmill. Over the 10 minutes, the speed of the treadmill is gradually increased so that the man has to work harder.

The graph below shows the amount of oxygen used by the man's body per minute during the exercise.

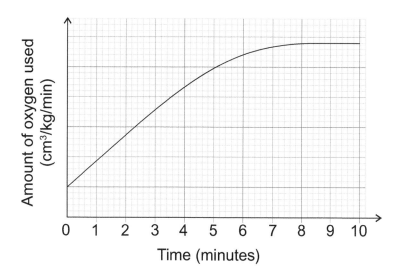

(i)   Describe what the graph shows during the first four minutes of exercise.

....

....   (1)

(ii)   Explain how the graph shows that the man was respiring anaerobically in the final two minutes of the exercise.

....

....

....

....

....   (2)

8. Smoking cigarettes can have many negative effects on a person's health.

When people smoke, they draw smoke from the cigarette into their lungs as they inhale.

(a) State what happens to the diaphragm as a person inhales.

.... (1)

Cigarettes contain the drug nicotine.

(b) State why nicotine can be described as a recreational drug.

....

.... (1)

(c) Many people find it difficult to stop smoking, even though they realise how bad it is for their health. Suggest why this is.

.... (1)

Smoking can lead to the development of emphysema.
Emphysema is a disease that destroys alveoli in the lungs.

(d) Explain why a person with emphysema may need to breathe more rapidly than a person without the disease.

....

....

....

....

.... (3)

Total marks: 60

SURNAME	....
FIRST NAME	....
JUNIOR SCHOOL	....
SENIOR SCHOOL	....

CGP practice exam paper for:

COMMON ENTRANCE 13+

SCIENCE

LEVEL 2

CHEMISTRY

Fill in your details in the spaces provided above.

Read this information before you start.

- Time allowed: 40 minutes.
- You should attempt **all** of the questions.
- You may use a calculator.

1. For each of the following, underline the option that best completes the sentence.

   (a) The chemical formula for hydrochloric acid is

   H_2Cl_2 HCl H_2Cl HCl_2

   (b) The percentage of air that is oxygen is

   18%   21%   31%   78%

   (c)

   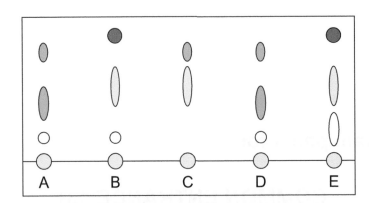

   The results for a chromatography investigation on five felt-tip pens are shown above. The results show that the two pens containing the same inks are

   A and B   **C and D**   **A and D**   **B and E**

   (d) A reaction between nitric acid and sodium carbonate will only produce

   a salt, water and carbon dioxide

   a salt and water

   a salt and carbon dioxide

   a salt and sulfuric acid

   (e) The reverse process of melting is called

   subliming

   condensing

   boiling

   freezing

(f)

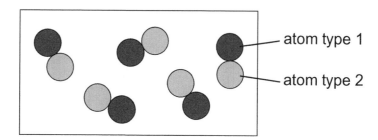

The diagram above shows

a molecule

an element

a compound

a mixture

(g) Thermal insulators are materials that don't conduct heat very well, such as

magnesium

sulfur

zinc

aluminium

(7)

2. Three identical iron nails are sealed in separate test tubes.

oil layer to keep air out

A — water, no air
B — air and water
C — air, no water

(a) What is the chemical symbol for iron?

.... (1)

The nails are left in a room of constant temperature for one week, and any change in appearance is recorded in the table below.

	Nail		
	A	B	C
Observations	No change.	Red-brown spots visible on surface.	No change.

(b) Explain what these results show about the conditions needed for iron to rust.

.... (1)

The experiment is repeated, but strips of magnesium are wrapped around the nails before they are sealed in the test tubes. Magnesium is more reactive than iron.

(c) Suggest how any observations in the table above may change.
Explain your answer.

....

.... (2)

Salt water can increase the rate at which iron rusts.

(d) Suggest how the original experiment could be modified to test this.

....

....

....

.... (2)

3.   Solid iodine can be used to observe changes in state.

(a)   Draw the arrangement of particles for solid iodine in the box below.

(1)

Some iodine crystals are heated in a beaker on a tripod over a Bunsen burner.
After a short time, the crystals begin to change into a purple gas.

(b)   (i)   Give the name of this process.

.... (1)

(ii)   Explain what happens during this process in terms of the particles in the solid.

....

....

....

.... (3)

(c)   Complete the sentences below by underlining the correct words.

When the iodine particles are in the gas state, they **collide** / **vibrate** with the beaker's walls

at **low** / **high** speed. This creates a **pulling** / **pushing** force on the walls of the beaker, known as

gas pressure.

(3)

4. Tim has one saucepan with a wooden handle, and another with an iron handle.
    When Tim is cooking, he notices that the iron handle is hot, but the wooden handle is not.

    Tim believes that the iron handle is hot because all metals are thermal conductors,
    and that the wooden handle is not hot because all non-metals are thermal insulators.

    Tim wants to see if he is right, so he sets up the following experiment.

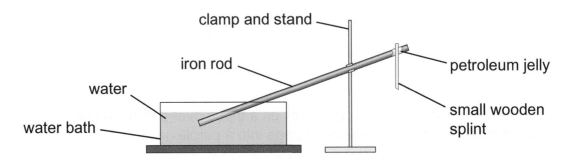

    Tim heats the water to boiling point and waits for 10 minutes. If the end of the rod that is out
    of the water gets hot, the petroleum jelly will melt and the splint will fall off. If it takes longer
    than 10 minutes for the splint to fall, Tim will assume that the rod cannot conduct heat.

    He repeats his experiment using a wooden rod.

    (a) (i) Write Tim's observation and his hypothesis for the experiment.

             observation: ....

             ....

             hypothesis: ....

             .... (2)

         (ii) Suggest a prediction for this experiment.

             ....

             ....

             .... (1)

    (b) Suggest why Tim uses a wooden splint and petroleum jelly instead of touching the rods
         to see if they're hot or not.

         ....

         .... (1)

Tim then repeats the experiment using a copper rod.
His results are shown in the table below.

Rod material	Did the wooden splint fall within 10 minutes?
Iron	Yes
Copper	Yes
Wood	No

Tim writes a conclusion for his experiment. In his conclusion he says:
'The results show that all metals conduct heat, and all non-metals don't conduct heat'.

(c)   Explain why Tim cannot reach this conclusion based on his results.

....

.... (1)

Tim does some research and finds that there are many conductive and physical differences between metals and non-metals.

(d)   Give two physical properties that are different between metals and non-metals.

1. ....

2. .... (2)

5.   A flask contains a small amount of salt dissolved in ethanol. A condenser can be used to separate the mixture. The set-up of this apparatus is shown below.

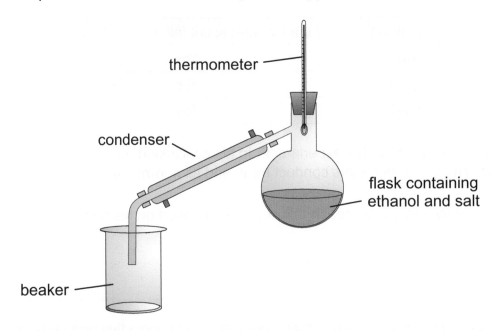

An electric water bath is used to boil the mixture in the flask.

(a)   Describe how heating the flask results in a sample of pure ethanol in the beaker.

State what a condenser is in your answer.

....

....

....

....

....

.... (4)

The following table gives the melting and boiling points of water, ethanol and salt.

Substance	Melting point (°C)	Boiling point (°C)
Water	0	100
Ethanol	−114	78
Salt	801	1413

(b)   State what minimum temperature the thermometer must read in the set-up above in order to obtain pure ethanol.

Temperature: .... °C   (1)

6. Hibo is investigating different reactions involving zinc.
    To start with, she adds a piece of zinc to a flask of hydrochloric acid.
    Bubbles of hydrogen gas are released, and zinc chloride is formed in solution.

    (a) Write the word equation to show the reaction described above.

    .... (1)

    The experimental set-up for Hibo's experiment is shown below.
    She measured the total mass as soon as the zinc was added to the hydrochloric acid,
    and again after 10 minutes, and found that the mass measured was different.

    (b) Explain this difference in mass.

    ....

    ....

    ....

    .... (2)

    Hibo then uses a separate reaction to make a sample of zinc oxide.

    (c) State and explain whether Hibo should react the zinc oxide
         with an acid or an alkali to produce a salt.

    ....

    .... (2)

    The melting point of zinc is 420 °C and the boiling point of zinc is 907 °C.

    (d) Suggest and explain whether the melting and boiling points of zinc oxide would be
         different to zinc.

    ....

    ....

    .... (2)

7. Charis investigated the rate of diffusion of ammonia along a glass tube.
    The apparatus she used for experiment A is shown below.

cotton wool with drops of ammonia
solution that give off ammonia gas   glass tube   damp red litmus paper

Ammonia is a weak alkali, so when the ammonia gas reaches the end of the tube,
the litmus paper changes colour. Charis timed how long this colour change took for
different numbers of drops of ammonia. Her results are shown in the table below.

Number of drops of ammonia solution	1	2	3	4	5
Time (s)	46	35	28	19	12

(a) Explain what the results tell you about the rate of diffusion of ammonia.
     Use the table to provide evidence for your explanation.

     ....

     ....

     ....

     .... (2)

(b) Give one variable that would need to be controlled to make this investigation a fair test.

     .... (1)

Charis carries out experiment B using cotton wool soaked with ammonia solution
at one end of the glass tube and cotton wool soaked in hydrochloric acid at the other end.
A ring of ammonium chloride forms closer to the end with the hydrochloric acid.

She then repeats experiment A, but uses cotton wool with drops of hydrochloric acid and
damp blue litmus paper.

(c) Suggest and explain how the results for time taken in experiment A
     will change when using hydrochloric acid instead of ammonia.

     ....

     ....

     ....

     ....

     ....

     .... (3)

8. Magnesium is a reactive metal.
   Reactive metals are sometimes stored in oil in science laboratories.

   (a) Suggest why reactive metals are sometimes stored in oil rather than in air.

   .... (1)

   A reaction takes place when magnesium is placed in dilute sulfuric acid.
   Louise wants to measure the amount of gas given out by the reaction
   using the set-up of equipment shown below.

   She drops a 2 cm strip of magnesium into a test tube containing 10 cm³ of sulfuric acid and
   puts a bung on top. She uses the gas syringe to measure the amount of gas given off by the
   reaction in a certain amount of time.

   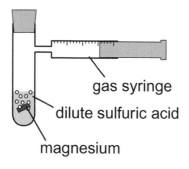

   gas syringe
   dilute sulfuric acid
   magnesium

   (b) (i) Complete the word equation for the reaction taking place.

   magnesium + sulfuric acid → .... + gas A (1)

   (ii) State what gas A is.

   .... (1)

   (iii) Describe how Louise could test for gas A.

   .... (1)

   Louise uses the set-up above to investigate how the concentration of the sulfuric acid affects
   the amount of gas A being released. She controls all of the relevant variables to make sure
   that the test is fair. Her results are shown in the table below.

Concentration of sulfuric acid (g/cm³)	Volume of gas produced (cm³)			
	Test 1	Test 2	Test 3	Mean
0.01	0.60	0.50	0.55	0.55
0.02	0.90	1.00	0.95	0.95
0.03	1.45	1.35	1.25	1.35
0.04	2.20	2.10	2.30	2.20
0.05	2.80	2.75	2.85	2.80

(c) (i) Plot Louise's results on the graph below.

Draw a line of best fit through your points.

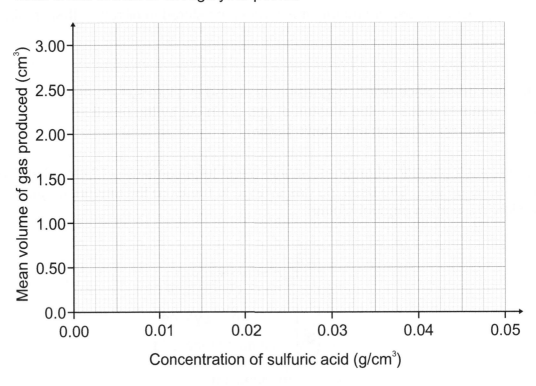

Concentration of sulfuric acid (g/cm³)

(3)

(ii) Using the graph drawn above, calculate the volume of gas A that would be given off for sulfuric acid with a concentration of 0.015 g/cm³.

(Show your working on the graph.)

Volume = ... cm³ (2)

Louise realises at the end of her experiment that the gas syringe always started with the plunger pulled out by 0.1 cm³, as shown below.

plunger pulled out by 0.1 cm³

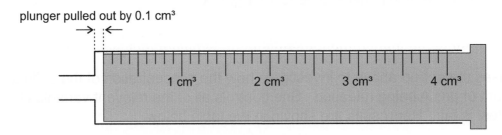

(d) (i) What type of error will this produce in Louise's results?

.... (1)

(ii) Describe how Louise could change all of her measurements of the volume of gas collected to correct for this.

.... (1)

9. The photograph shows the NASA Space Shuttle soon after being launched.

A hydrocarbon called kerosene can be used to fuel rockets.
Kerosene burns in oxygen to form carbon dioxide and water vapour.

(a) Suggest another substance that would be produced in this reaction if the
kerosene contained sulfur impurities.

.... (1)

Rockets are propelled up into the atmosphere and out into space.
There is less oxygen available higher up in the atmosphere, further away from the Earth.

(b) Suggest why carbon monoxide is also sometimes produced by
kerosene-fuelled rockets.

....

.... (1)

(c) Describe a test that could be carried out to show that a sample of
an unknown gas is carbon dioxide, including what would be observed.

....

.... (1)

Total marks: 60

CGP practice exam paper for:

COMMON ENTRANCE 13+

SCIENCE

LEVEL 2

PHYSICS

Fill in your details in the spaces provided above.

Read this information before you start.

- Time allowed: 40 minutes.
- You should attempt **all** of the questions.
- You may use a calculator.

1. For each of the following, underline the option that best completes the sentence.

(a) A unit of density is

kg/m³   **kg/m²**   **m³/kg**   **kgm²**

(b) A student measures the current in a series circuit as she adds components to the circuit. The table below shows her results.

Number of components added	1	2	3	4	5
Current / A	11.2	9.4	7.5	6.0	4.9

The results show that

as the number of components increases, the current increases

as the number of components increases, the current decreases

there is no relationship between the number of components and the current

the investigation was a fair test

(c) When light crosses a boundary at an angle, it can bend, as shown in the diagram below.

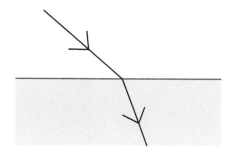

This is called

absorption   **refraction**   **emission**   **reflection**

(d) An example of a satellite is the

Solar System   **Sun**   **Moon**   **Milky Way**

(e) Energy is always

destroyed   **created**   **conserved**   **useful**

(f)   A train moves in one direction along a track.
       A force diagram of the forces acting on a train is shown below.

The diagram tells you that

the train is moving backwards at a steady speed

the forces acting on the train are balanced

the speed of the train is changing

the train is moving forward at a steady speed

(g)   The symbol for an electrical component is shown below.

The symbol represents a

bulb   **buzzer**   **motor**   **cell**

(7)

2. Rashmi lives in England. Her friend Manuel lives in Ecuador.
   Ecuador is a country which lies on the Earth's equator.

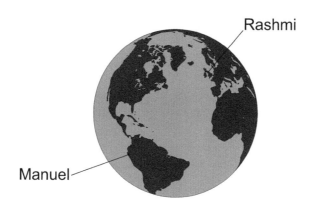

It is summer in England. The days are eighteen hours long.
In Ecuador the days are always around twelve hours long.

(a) Explain why when it's summer in England, the days are longer than in Ecuador.

   ....

   ....

   .... (2)

It is possible for a lunar eclipse to take place that both Rashmi and Manuel can observe.

(b) Describe the position of the Earth in relation to the Sun and the Moon during
    a lunar eclipse.

   ....

   .... (1)

(c) Suggest why a solar eclipse that Manuel observes in Ecuador will not be visible
    for Rashmi in England.

   ....

   ....

   ....

   .... (2)

3. Some electricity in the UK is generated from non-renewable energy resources.
    The UK also uses renewable energy resources, such as solar and biomass.

    (a) Give one advantage and one disadvantage of using non-renewable
         energy resources to generate electricity.

         Advantage: ....

         ....

         Disadvantage: ....

         .... (2)

    The amount of electricity generated from solar power during summer is
    always larger than the amount generated during winter of the same year.

    (b) Suggest a reason for this.

         ....

         .... (1)

    To generate electricity using biomass as fuel, the biomass is burnt.
    The energy released is used to heat water, which changes into steam.
    This steam is used to drive a turbine attached to a generator, which generates electricity
    when it spins.

    (c) Describe the useful energy transfer that takes place between
         the biomass and water when generating electricity.

         ....

         .... (2)

    (d) State where the energy released from biomass ultimately comes from.

         .... (1)

    An island community wants to generate renewable power. The island is located in a wet
    and cloudy climate. It rains frequently there and the soil is very fertile.

    (e) Give one reason why the community might choose biomass rather than solar for
         generating electricity.

         ....

         .... (1)

4. Workers in a shoe factory use a tool to make holes in leather. The tool is shown below.
    To punch a hole, a worker pushes the handle down.

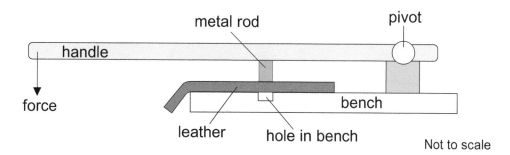

A worker pushes on the handle, causing the metal rod to push on the leather with a force of 80 N. The end of the metal rod has an area of 0.5 cm².

(a) Calculate the pressure exerted on the leather by the rod.

Pressure = ... N/cm² (2)

If the pressure is not large enough, the tool will not punch the leather.

(b) Give one change that could be made to the tool to increase the pressure on the leather for the same amount of force applied.

.... (1)

A new machine is developed that automatically punches the holes.
The force applied by the machine is tested and the results are shown in the table below.

Test	Force applied (N)
1	84.1
2	83.6
3	84.4
4	83.9

(c) (i) Calculate the mean force applied by the machine using the results in the table.

Mean force applied = ... N (1)

The average pressure exerted by the new machine is 140 N/cm².

(ii) Use this information and your answer to (i) to estimate the area of the end of the metal rod on the new machine.

Area = ... cm² (2)

5.   Aled is carrying out an experiment to investigate how the force acting on
     a spring affects the spring's extension. He sets up the equipment below.

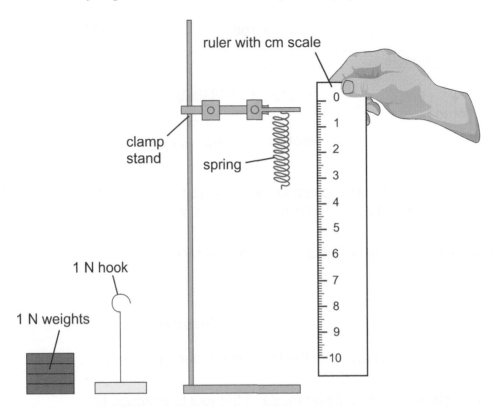

Aled records the position of the bottom of the spring on the ruler, then adds
a 1 N hook and records the new position. He subtracts the original position
from the new position to calculate the extension. He then adds 1 N weights
one at a time, and measures the extension each time.

(a)   Suggest how his experimental set-up could be improved.

....   (1)

The independent variable in this experiment is the total weight on the end of the spring.

(b)   Explain why all other variables in the experiment should be kept constant.

....   (1)

On Earth, gravity exerts a force of 10 N on 1 kg.

(c)   Show that the mass of one of the weights is 0.1 kg.

(2)

(2)

The results for Aled's experiment are shown in the table below.

Weight (N)	Extension (cm)			
	Repeat 1	Repeat 2	Repeat 3	Mean
1	1.3	1.4	1.5	1.4
2	2.6	2.9	2.9	2.8
3	4.3	4.2	3.8	4.1
4	5.6	5.4	5.8	5.6
5	6.9	7.2	6.9	7.0

(d) Plot the data on the graph below. Draw a line of best fit.

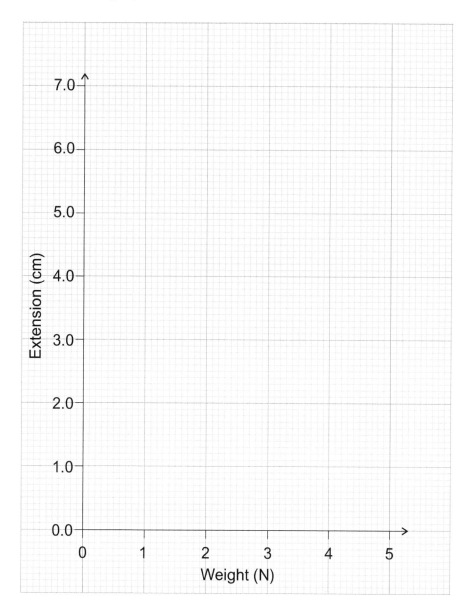

(2)

(e)   Use the data to write a conclusion for Aled's experiment.

....

....

....

....   (2)

(f)   Complete the following sentence using one of the words below.

precise	systematic	accurate	fair

When Aled repeated the investigation, he got very similar results.

This means Aled's results are ....   (1)

6. The diagram shows an electromagnet used to control a device for locking a door.

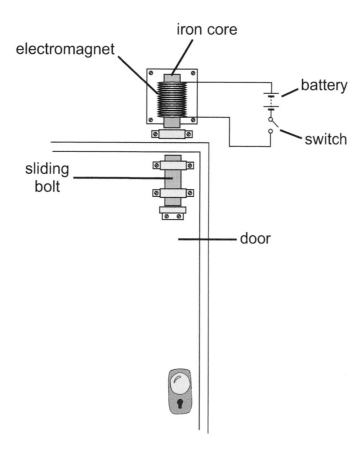

When the electromagnet is switched on, the door is locked.
When the electromagnet is switched off, the door is unlocked.

(a) Describe how turning the switch on locks the door.

....

....

.... (2)

(b) Complete the sentence below by underlining the correct words.

The weight of the bolt is **smaller** / **greater** than the force of **attraction** / **repulsion** from the

electromagnet when the door is locked. (2)

It takes 0.05 s from the moment the switch is turned on for the bolt to close the gap and lock the door. The gap between the bolt and the electromagnet when the door is unlocked is 5 cm.

(c) (i) Calculate the speed of the bolt in m/s when the switch is turned on.

.... m/s (3)

(ii) Suggest one way you could adapt the circuit to make the door lock more quickly.

.... (1)

The switch in the circuit is replaced with a different type of switch.
A second switch, of the same type, is also added to the circuit.
The circuit now needs people on both sides of the door to push down on a switch to lock it.

(d) Complete the circuit diagram for this circuit.
    The electromagnet has been drawn for you.

(2)

7. Kirstie is investigating sound waves.
   She has an oscilloscope, like the one shown in the photo.

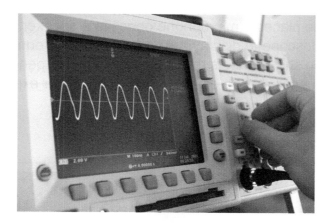

The diagram below shows the display from the oscilloscope as a sound is played.

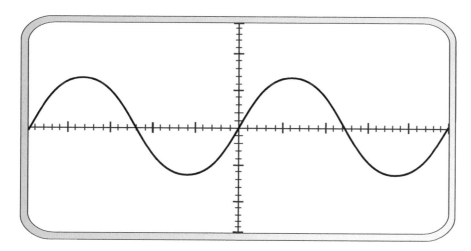

(a) Draw on the same diagram what you would expect to see if the
    same sound was played more quietly. (2)

Kirstie played the sound to several people all at once.
None of the people had ever reported having difficulty hearing.

(b) Suggest why not all of the people would be able to hear the sound.

   ....

   ....

   .... (2)

Kirstie wants to investigate whether there is a relationship between the frequency of a sound wave and its amplitude.

For her investigation she places a microphone opposite a speaker. She connects the microphone to the oscilloscope to display the sound waves. Frequency will be her independent variable, so she connects the speaker to a signal generator which can create sounds at different frequencies. The diagram below shows her experimental set-up.

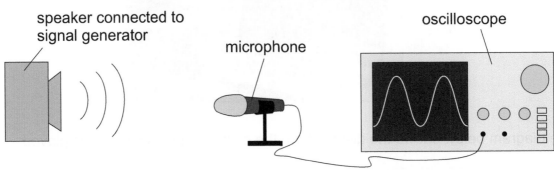

(c) (i) State what the dependent variable in Kirstie's investigation will be.

.... (1)

(ii) Describe how Kirstie can use her experimental set-up for the investigation. State two variables she will have to control.

....

....

....

....

....

....

.... (4)

Kirstie discovers that the there is no relationship between the frequency of a sound wave and its amplitude.

(d) Give one way in which Kirstie could check that her results were repeatable.

.... (1)

(e) Describe how the speed of the sound waves transmitted by the speaker would differ if Kirstie carried out her investigation in water instead of air.

.... (1)

8. The photograph below shows a plotting compass.

The needle of a compass is a small bar magnet.

(a) Explain why the needle points North if the compass isn't close to a magnet.

.... (1)

A compass is placed next to a bar magnet, as shown in the diagram below.

N   S

compass   bar magnet

(b) Draw an arrow in the compass to show which way the needle would point.   (1)

The compass is used to reveal the shape of the bar magnet's magnetic field.
Magnetic fields can be represented by magnetic field lines.
Magnetic field lines have arrows which show you the direction of the magnetic field.

(c) What else do magnetic field lines tell you about a magnetic field?

.... (1)

(d) Explain how you could use the bar magnet above to test whether
     another material is a magnet.

....

....

.... (2)

Total marks: 60

Answers

Section B1 — Cells, Nutrients and Healthy Living

Page 3 — Cells

1 a) cell wall: gives support to the cell *[1 mark]*
cell surface membrane: holds the cell together and controls what goes in and out *[1 mark]*
mitochondria: carries out most of the reactions for aerobic respiration / releases energy for the cell *[1 mark]*
chloroplast: makes food for the plant by photosynthesis *[1 mark]*

   b) vacuole *[1 mark]*

   c) i) cytoplasm *[1 mark]*
ii) It is where most chemical reactions happen *[1 mark]*.

Page 4 — More on Cells

1 a) cell — tissue — organ — organism *[1 mark]*

   b) A group of organs working together *[1 mark]*.

2 a) excretion *[1 mark]*

   b) sensitivity *[1 mark]*

   c) Any two from: respiration / growth / nutrition / reproduction / movement *[1 mark for two correct]*

Pages 5-6 — The Light Microscope

1 a) E.g. take a small sample of the onion cells and place it in the middle of a clean microscope slide *[1 mark]*. Use a pipette to add a drop of water to the sample *[1 mark]*. Carefully put a clean coverslip over the top *[1 mark]*.

   b) She should be careful not to reflect direct sunlight into the microscope as it could damage her eyes *[1 mark]*.

   c) E.g. turn the rough focusing knob to move the objective lens down to just above the slide *[1 mark]*. Then use the fine focusing knob to adjust the focus until a clear image of the cells is visible *[1 mark]*.

   d) E.g. eosin Y / iodine / methylene blue *[1 mark]*

   e) × 1000 *[1 mark]*
The total magnification is the eyepiece lens magnification × the objective lens magnification.

2 a) image size = magnification × real size
= 40 × 3
= 120 mm
[2 marks for the correct answer, otherwise 1 mark for correctly rearranging the formula]

   b) Any three from: e.g. by using clear, unbroken lines. / By avoiding colouring/shading. / By making his drawing take up at least half of the space available. / By using straight lines for labels. / By making sure label lines don't cross over each other. / By including the magnification in the title. *[3 marks available — 1 mark for each correct answer]*

Page 7 — Nutrition

1 a) energy *[1 mark]*

   b) growth and repair of tissues *[1 mark]*

   c) energy and insulation *[1 mark]*

2 a)

Food Source	Component
Oranges	Vitamins
Butter	Lipids / fats and oils
Fish	Proteins
Cup of coffee	Water
Potatoes	Carbohydrates
Table salt	Minerals
Carrots	Fibre

[6 marks — 1 mark for each correct answer]

   b) E.g. because all chemical reactions in the body take place in water *[1 mark]*.

Page 8 — Staying Healthy

1 a) i) mineral *[1 mark]*
ii) A lack of calcium can lead to osteoporosis / can reduce bone density and make bones more likely to fracture / can lead to rickets *[1 mark]*.

   b) scurvy *[1 mark]*

2 a) The body doesn't get enough energy from food and starts to use up its lipid stores *[1 mark]*. This can cause the person to lose weight and feel weak and tired / lead to starvation *[1 mark]*.

   b) i) E.g. high blood pressure *[1 mark]* and heart disease *[1 mark]*
ii) Meal B *[1 mark]*
iii) It can increase your blood cholesterol level, which increases the risk of heart disease *[1 mark]*.

Page 9 — Food Tests

1 a) E.g. transfer the ground up bread to a beaker and add some distilled water *[1 mark]*. Stir the mixture with a glass rod to dissolve some of it *[1 mark]*. Filter the solution using a funnel lined with filter paper to get rid of the solid bits of bread *[1 mark]*.

   b) Benedict's solution *[1 mark]*

   c) iodine solution *[1 mark]*

   d) i) ethanol *[1 mark]*
ii) The sample contains lipids *[1 mark]*.

   e) She would place the sample in a test tube with biuret solution *[1 mark]* and shake it to mix the contents *[1 mark]*. If protein is present, the solution will change from blue to purple *[1 mark]*.

Page 10 — Drugs

1 All drugs are smoked. *[1 mark]*
E.g. alcohol is a drug that isn't smoked.

2 E.g. people can become addicted to some medical drugs *[1 mark]*.

3 a) Drugs that are used for enjoyment, rather than as medicine *[1 mark]*.

b) E.g. tobacco smoke contains chemicals like tar *[1 mark]*, which damage the lungs *[1 mark]*.

c) i) E.g. drinking too much alcohol could lead to health problems such as cirrhosis/liver disease *[1 mark]*. It also impairs judgement, which can lead to accidents *[1 mark]*.

ii) E.g. marijuana can cause hallucinations *[1 mark]*. It can also cause mental health problems, such as anxiety and paranoia *[1 mark]*.

Page 11 — Preventing Disease

1 a) i) e.g. colds / flu / chickenpox / German measles *[1 mark]*

ii) e.g. tetanus / food poisoning / whooping cough *[1 mark]*

b) E.g. viruses invade living tissue and damage cells *[1 mark]*.

2 a) E.g. washing hands washes off the micro-organisms that cling to our skin when we touch things *[1 mark]*. Doing this before eating means the micro-organisms don't get onto the food, so they don't enter our bodies *[1 mark]*.

b) E.g. covering your mouth and nose with a tissue when sneezing or coughing and then binning the tissue *[1 mark]*.

c) E.g. places where food is made or prepared need to be kept clean *[1 mark]* to prevent harmful micro-organisms getting into the food *[1 mark]*. / Rubbish should be disposed of properly and collected regularly so that it doesn't build up *[1 mark]*. A build-up of rubbish can result in the harmful micro-organisms that grow on it being passed onto humans by the animals that feed on the rubbish *[1 mark]*.

Section B2 — Breathing and Reproduction

Pages 12-13 — Breathing

1 a) backbone/spine *[1 mark]*

b) When the rubber band is no longer stretched, the horizontal rods will be pulled upwards *[1 mark]*. This represents the ribs being pulled upwards *[1 mark]* because of the contraction of the intercostal muscles when a person breathes in *[1 mark]*.

2 a) i) the balloons *[1 mark]*

ii) rubber sheet *[1 mark]*

iii) bell jar *[1 mark]*

b) Pulling down the rubber sheet increases the volume inside the bell jar, which decreases the pressure *[1 mark]*. The drop in pressure causes air to rush into the balloons *[1 mark]*.

3 a) rib/rib cage *[1 mark]*

b) diaphragm *[1 mark]*

c) It moves down *[1 mark]*, which causes the volume of the chest to increase *[1 mark]*. This decreases the pressure in the chest, so air rushes in to fill the lungs *[1 mark]*.

d) The diaphragm relaxes/moves up and the external intercostal muscles relax *[1 mark]*. This decreases the volume of the chest *[1 mark]*, which increases the pressure in the chest, causing air to rush out of the lungs *[1 mark]*.

Page 14 — More on Breathing

1 a) $(450 + 525 + 470 + 485 + 415) \div 5 = 469 \text{ cm}^3$ *[1 mark]*.

b) Taking repeated measurements can improve accuracy *[1 mark]*. It can also make the results more reliable *[1 mark]*.

c) Jackson's results are not precise because they are quite spread out from the mean *[1 mark]*.

d) She needs to take the biggest breath in possible *[1 mark]* then breathe out as hard and quickly as possible into the peak flow meter and read the value off the scale *[1 mark]*.

Vital capacity is the total amount of air a person can breathe out after taking their biggest breath in.

e) The muscles around her bronchioles may contract *[1 mark]* which would narrow her airways *[1 mark]*. The lining of the airways may become inflamed and fluid may build up in the airways *[1 mark]*.

f) E.g. smoking / drug use / air pollution / dust or fumes *[1 mark]*.

Pages 15-16 — Human Reproductive Systems

1 a) ovaries *[1 mark]*

b) 28 days *[1 mark]*

2 a)

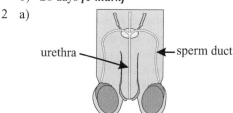

urethra — sperm duct

[2 marks — 1 mark for each correct label]

b) It carries sperm through the penis during ejaculation. / Urine passes through it to exit the body *[1 mark]*.

c) sperm *[1 mark]*

d) i) They produce sperm *[1 mark]*.

ii) It produces the liquid that is added to sperm to make semen *[1 mark]*.

3 A: uterus/womb *[1 mark]*

B: vagina *[1 mark]*

C: fallopian tube *[1 mark]*

D: ovary *[1 mark]*

4 a) Sperm are released from the penis into the vagina *[1 mark]*. The sperm then travel to the fallopian tubes where they meet the egg *[1 mark]*.

b) There are millions of sperm and only one egg *[1 mark]*.

c) The head of a sperm breaks through the membrane of the egg cell *[1 mark]*. The nuclei of the sperm and egg cell then fuse together *[1 mark]*.

Page 17 — Having a Baby

1 a) placenta *[1 mark]*

   b) E.g. it protects the fetus from knocks and bumps *[1 mark]*.

   c) i) The placenta lets the blood of the fetus and the blood of the mother get very close together *[1 mark]*. Alcohol in the mother's blood can cross the placenta to get to the fetus *[1 mark]*.

   ii) E.g. it could cause the baby to have a low birth weight *[1 mark]*.

   d) The fertilised egg/zygote divides and once it is a ball of cells it's called an embryo *[1 mark]*.

Page 18 — The Menstrual Cycle

1 a) i) B *[1 mark]*

   ii) A *[1 mark]*

   iii)D *[1 mark]*

   iv) D *[1 mark]*

   b) So that the uterus is ready to receive a fertilised egg *[1 mark]*.

   c) 10 days *[1 mark]*

   d) Day 14 *[1 mark]*

Pages 19-21 — Plant Reproduction, Fertilisation and Seed Dispersal

1 a) E *[1 mark]*

   b) A *[1 mark]*

   c) i) E.g. scented flowers/bright coloured petals/nectar *[1 mark]*

   ii) anther *[1 mark]* and stigma *[1 mark]*

   d) Wind pollination *[1 mark]*. E.g. the flower's filaments may be longer so that the anthers stick outside the flower, so pollen gets blown away from the anthers *[1 mark]*. The flower may also have feathery stigmas to catch the pollen blown from anthers *[1 mark]*.

2 a) Pollination is where pollen grains are transferred from an anther to a stigma *[1 mark]*.

   b) A pollen tube grows out of a pollen grain, down through the style and into the ovary *[1 mark]*. The nucleus from a male gamete inside the pollen grain *[1 mark]* moves down the pollen tube to the ovule *[1 mark]*.

3 a) Seeds need to be dispersed so that they can grow without too much competition *[1 mark]* from the parent plant and from each other *[1 mark]*.

   b) Tomato: This is animal-dispersed. The fruit is brightly coloured to attract animals to eat it *[1 mark]*. Dandelion: This is wind-dispersed. It has a parachute so it can catch the wind to be carried away *[1 mark]*.

   c) E.g. the fruit explodes/bursts open once it has ripened, scattering the seeds away from the parent plant. / The fruit falls from the parent plant then rolls away *[1 mark]*.

4 a) wind dispersal *[1 mark]*

   b) i) The distance to which seeds are dispersed *[1 mark]*.

   ii) The length/size of the model wings *[1 mark]*.

   c) i) 30 – 7 = 23 cm *[1 mark]*

   ii) E.g. the larger the sycamore fruit the further the fruit is dispersed *[1 mark]*.

d) E.g. by repeating their measurements three times and taking an average *[1 mark]*.

Section B3 — Photosynthesis and Respiration

Page 22 — Plant Nutrition

1 a) i) water *[1 mark]*

   ii) chlorophyll *[1 mark]*

   b) carbon dioxide + water ⟶ glucose + oxygen *[1 mark]*

   c) E.g. to produce new biomass/to grow *[1 mark]*

2 a) Plants A and D *[1 mark]*. They are roughly the same shape and size and so it will be a fair test *[1 mark]*.

   b) Water one of the plants once a week and one twice a week *[1 mark]*. Measure the height of both plants, e.g. once a week, to track the speed of growth of the plants *[1 mark]*.

Pages 23-24 — Photosynthesis Experiments

1 a) Support: E.g. The rate of photosynthesis increases with light intensity between A and C *[1 mark]*. Does not support: E.g. The rate of photosynthesis does not increase between C and D *[1 mark]*.

   b) E.g. put the plant under a funnel in a beaker *[1 mark]*. Fill the beaker with a solution of sodium hydrogen carbonate to provide carbon dioxide and water *[1 mark]*. Put a measuring cylinder over the top *[1 mark]*. Leave it for 12 hours and use a measuring cylinder to measure the volume of oxygen produced *[1 mark]*.

   c) i) To make it a fair test *[1 mark]*.

   ii) Any two from: e.g. temperature, carbon dioxide level in the water, length of time the plant is left for, the plant used *[2 marks]*.

2 a) chlorophyll *[1 mark]*

   b) Plants use starch to store glucose produced during photosynthesis *[1 mark]*.

   c) So that she can compare the amount of starch in a green and non-green part of a leaf *[1 mark]*.

   d) Blue/black *[1 mark]*

   e) Boil the leaf in water for a few minutes to soften it *[1 mark]*. Put the leaf in a boiling tube with ethanol and place in hot water to boil the ethanol and remove the chlorophyll from the leaf *[1 mark]*. Dip the leaf in water to wash it *[1 mark]*.

   f) Area A will be blue/black because that area is able to photosynthesise and produce starch *[1 mark]*. Area B will be brown because it is unable to photosynthesise (due to the lack of chlorophyll) so no starch will be produced and so the iodine solution won't change colour *[1 mark]*.

Page 25 — The Importance of Plants

1 algae *[1 mark]*

2   The crop uses energy from sunlight to make glucose during photosynthesis *[1 mark]*. The plants use this glucose to make the organic molecules that store the Sun's energy *[1 mark]*. This energy is passed on to the chickens when they eat the grain *[1 mark]*.

3   a) Mouse A collapsed because it had used a lot of the oxygen in the jar for respiration *[1 mark]*. In the other jar, the plant took in carbon dioxide and gave out oxygen during photosynthesis *[1 mark]*. This provided a greater supply of oxygen to mouse B, which could therefore respire for longer without collapsing *[1 mark]*.
    b) It shows that plants are essential in maintaining the levels of oxygen and carbon dioxide needed for animals to survive *[1 mark]*.

Page 26 — Aerobic Respiration
1   a) Put a straw in the test tube, take a deep breath and then breathe out into the tube *[1 mark]*.
    b) orange/yellow *[1 mark]*
2   a) Breathing is moving air in and out of the lungs *[1 mark]*, and respiration is a chemical reaction that releases energy from food *[1 mark]*.
    b) glucose + oxygen → carbon dioxide + water *[1 mark]*
    c) mitochondria *[1 mark]*
    d) Glucose comes from eating food, and oxygen is breathed in from the air *[1 mark]*. They are transported in the blood *[1 mark]*.
    e) E.g. building proteins / muscle contraction / keeping warm *[1 mark]*

Page 27 — Anaerobic Respiration
1   a) E.g. aerobic respiration requires oxygen, anaerobic doesn't *[1 mark]*. Aerobic respiration produces carbon dioxide and water, whereas anaerobic respiration produces lactic acid *[1 mark]*. Aerobic respiration releases more energy than anaerobic respiration (for every glucose molecule used) *[1 mark]*.
    b) glucose → carbon dioxide + alcohol/ethanol *[1 mark]*
2   a) In normal conditions spaces in the soil are filled with air. This means root cells can respire **aerobically**. If there is prolonged heavy rainfall, soils can become waterlogged. This means the spaces in the soil fill up with water. When this happens, root cells have to respire **anaerobically**. *[2 marks]*
    b) E.g. the pencil-like roots stay above the water so that they can take in oxygen from the air *[1 mark]*. This allows the root cells to respire aerobically which releases more energy from glucose than anaerobic respiration *[1 mark]*.

Page 28 — Fermentation
1   a) sugar/glucose *[1 mark]*
    b) E.g. the balloon will inflate *[1 mark]*. When yeast respire they produce gas/carbon dioxide *[1 mark]*. As the balloon is covering the mouth of the bottle, the gas/carbon dioxide will be trapped and so will start to fill the balloon *[1 mark]*.

    c) E.g. yeast is used in bread making and brewing. The gas/carbon dioxide produced by the yeast respiring causes bubbles to form in beer, making it fizzy *[1 mark]*. In bread making, the gas/carbon dioxide produced is trapped in bubbles in the dough, which makes the bread rise. *[1 mark]*
    d) E.g. she could repeat the experiment at different temperatures *[1 mark]* and time how long it took for the balloon to fill to a certain size *[1 mark]*. She would need to use the same size bottles and balloons. She would also need to use the same amount of yeast, water and sugar in each bottle *[2 marks for at least three correct control variables, otherwise 1 mark for two correct control variables]*.

Section B4 — Interdependence and Populations

Pages 29-30 — Interdependence and Food Webs
1   a) producers *[1 mark]*
    b) primary consumer *[1 mark]*
2   a) All the living organisms in an area, plus their habitat *[1 mark]*.
    b) seagull *[1 mark]*
    c) E.g. a food chain only has one producer, while a food web can have several producers *[1 mark]*.
    You would get the mark here for any sensible comparison.
    d)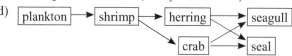

    [1 mark for arrow from shrimp to crab, 1 mark for arrows from crab to seagull and seal, 1 mark for arrow from herring to seal.]
3   a) E.g. the organisms need each other to survive *[1 mark]*.
    b)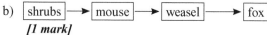
        [1 mark]
    c) i) rabbits, squirrels, mice, weasels *[1 mark]*
        ii) mouse *[1 mark]*
    d) Result: The number of rabbits would increase. Explanation: There would be more food available *[1 mark]*.
    e) Reason for increase: e.g. the amount of shrubs might increase as there will be no mice to eat them *[1 mark]*. So the number of squirrels might increase because there will be more food available *[1 mark]*. Reason for decrease: e.g. the number of weasels might decrease as there are no mice for them to eat *[1 mark]*. So the number of squirrels might decrease because they will be more likely to be eaten by foxes (since the foxes will have fewer weasels to eat) *[1 mark]*.

Page 31 — Investigating Populations
1   a) i) pitfall traps *[1 mark]*
        ii) Pitfall traps can be placed into a hole in the ground, with the top partly open *[1 mark]*. When woodlice fall into the trap, they are unable to get out (because of the steep sides of the container) and so you can count them *[1 mark]*.

b) E.g. repeat the investigation three times and calculate a mean number of woodlice *[1 mark]*.

2 a) quadrat *[1 mark]*

    b) $(12 + 8 + 9 + 4 + 7) \div 5 = 40 \div 5 = 8$ *[2 marks for the correct answer, otherwise 1 mark for correct working]*

    c) $8 \times 32 = 256$ buttercups *[1 mark]*

Page 32 — Protecting Living Things

1 a) E.g. the population size of orang-utans could decrease because there would be less food available for them to eat *[1 mark]*, so they might not all be able to survive and reproduce successfully *[1 mark]*.

    b) Humans use **resources** from the Earth to survive. Human activity has led to **pollution** of the environment and damage to many **habitats**. The human population is **increasing**. So we need to manage the way we use resources to meet our needs without destroying things for future **generations** — this is called **sustainable** development.
  [6 marks — 1 mark for each correct word]

2 a) The zoo could breed the oryx in captivity, where they won't be hunted *[1 mark]*. These new oryx could then be released into the wild *[1 mark]*.

    b) E.g. protect their habitat from hunters *[1 mark]*.

Section B5 — Variation and Classification

Pages 33-34 — Variation

1 a) Discontinuous *[1 mark]*

    b) The variation is discontinuous because there are just four distinct options, not a whole continuous range *[1 mark]*.

2 a) Any two from: e.g. the quality of the soil in which the sunflowers were planted may have been different. / The sunflowers may have been exposed to different amounts of sunlight while growing. / The sunflowers may have received different amounts of water while growing. / The temperature experienced by the sunflowers may have been different.
  [2 marks — 1 mark for each correct answer].

    b) i) Continuous variation *[1 mark]*

       ii) Any two from: e.g. weight / skin colour / hand span
  [2 marks — 1 mark for each correct answer].

3 a) E.g.

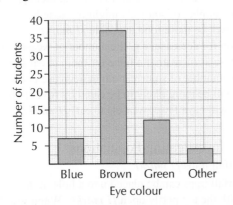

[3 marks — 1 mark for all bars plotted correctly, 1 mark for axes labelled correctly, 1 mark for sensible scale.]

b) In total there are $7 + 37 + 12 + 4 = 60$ students. Percentage with green eyes $= (12 \div 60) \times 100 = 20\%$ *[1 mark]*

c) E.g. measure the heights up against a wall *[1 mark]* to make sure the ruler/tape measure is vertical *[1 mark]*. Press a flat board onto the student's head *[1 mark]* to flatten down any hair/to make sure the highest point of the body is measured *[1 mark]*.
Any sensible suggestion of how to take accurate measurements with an explanation would be awarded marks for this question.

Page 35 — Classification

1 Bacteria *[1 mark]*, protists *[1 mark]*

2 a) i) Insects *[1 mark]*

       ii) It has 6 legs / a 3-part body / 1 pair of antennae *[1 mark]*

    b) i) Arachnids *[1 mark]*

       ii) It has 8 legs / a 2-part body / no antennae *[1 mark]*

3 a) Animals *[1 mark]*

    b) Reptiles *[1 mark]*

    c) Mammals *[1 mark]*

Page 36 — Structures of Different Organisms

1 a)

Kingdom	Single-celled?	Cells have a nucleus?	Cells have a cell wall?	Able to move around?
Animals	No	**Yes**	No	Yes
Fungi	Can be	Yes	Yes	**No**
Plants	No	Yes	**Yes**	No

[2 marks for all four correct, otherwise 1 mark for at least two correct]

    b) Any two from: plants / bacteria / protists
  [2 marks — 1 mark for each correct answer]

2 a) Having webbed feet will help the penguin to swim / walk on soft ground *[1 mark]*.

    b) E.g. the penguin has a pointed beak *[1 mark]*, which may help it to catch prey *[1 mark]*. / The penguin has flippers/a tail *[1 mark]*, which may help it to swim to find food/mates *[1 mark]*.

Section C1 — States of Matter

Page 37 — The Particle Model

1 a) State of matter: liquid *[1 mark]*
  Reasoning: because the particles are close but are able to move past one another / are not in a regular arrangement *[1 mark]*.

    b) The forces of attraction between solid particles are strong *[1 mark]*, so the particles are held closely together in fixed positions *[1 mark]*. The forces in liquids and gases are weaker *[1 mark]*, so the particles can move past one another/flow to take the shape of the container *[1 mark]*.

2 a) Syringe B, because particles are closer together in liquids than in gases *[1 mark]*, so more particles of liquid can fit into a set volume *[1 mark]*.

    b) i) E.g. pull the plunger outwards *[1 mark]*.

       ii) No. The forces of attraction between particles stop the liquid from expanding *[1 mark]*.

Page 38 — Changes of State

1 a) A: melting *[1 mark]*
        B: freezing *[1 mark]*
        C: condensing *[1 mark]*
   b) Evaporation occurs slowly at any temperature
        [1 mark], whereas boiling occurs rapidly at the
        boiling point of a substance *[1 mark]*.
2 a) i) When heated, iodine will change state from a **solid**
            to a **gas** *[1 mark]*.
       ii) When cooled, iodine will change state from a **gas**
            to a **solid** *[1 mark]*.
   b) i) The particles move less *[1 mark]* and move closer
            together *[1 mark]*.
       ii) The particles move less because they have less
            energy at a lower temperature *[1 mark]*. This
            strengthens the forces holding the particles
            together, which causes them to move closer together
            [1 mark].

Pages 39-40 — Gas Pressure and Diffusion

1 a) The air particles bounce off the sides of the mattress
        at high speeds, creating a pushing force/pressure
        [1 mark].
   b) The pressure increases *[1 mark]*. This is because
        if there's more air in the mattress, there are more
        particles bouncing off the sides of the mattress
        [1 mark].
2 a) The spreading out of the particles of potassium
        manganate(VII) from a small initial area of high
        concentration *[1 mark]* to other parts of the water
        where they are at a lower concentration *[1 mark]*.
   b) The potassium manganate(VII) particles bump into
        each other, as well as water particles, which stops them
        from spreading more quickly *[1 mark]*.
   c) i) water temperature *[1 mark]*.
       ii) time taken for the potassium manganate(VII) to
            diffuse *[1 mark]*.
       iii) mass of potassium manganate(VII) *[1 mark]*.
   *Remember, the independent variable is the thing you change,
   the dependent variable is the thing you measure, and the
   control variables are the things you keep the same.*
   d) E.g. it can increase the accuracy of the results
        [1 mark]. It can also increase the reliability of the
        results *[1 mark]*.
   e) mean = (108 + 134 + 127) ÷ 3 = 123 s *[1 mark]*
   f) E.g. the potassium manganate(VII) diffuses faster in
        water at 70 °C than in water at 20 °C *[1 mark]*. The
        diffusion rate is approximately twice as fast at 70 °C
        than at 20 °C *[1 mark]*.
   g) E.g. she could repeat the experiment at other
        temperatures *[1 mark]*.
   *This would allow her to see a pattern in her results, e.g. by
   plotting a temperature-time graph. This wouldn't be valid if
   she did this with her current method, as there are only two
   data points/temperatures.*

Section C2 — Atoms, Elements, Molecules and Compounds

Page 41 — Atoms and Elements

1 a) Different elements contain **different types of atom**
        [1 mark].
   b) The elements are organised in the **periodic table**
        [1 mark].
   c) The number of known elements is approximately **100**
        [1 mark].
2 a) C *[1 mark]*
   b) Cl *[1 mark]*
   c) Ca *[1 mark]*
   d) Cu *[1 mark]*
3 a) An atom is a type of tiny particle *[1 mark]*.
   b) An element is a substance that contains only one type
        of atom *[1 mark]*.

Page 42 — Compounds

1 a)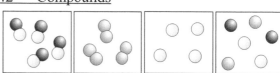
        compound   element   element   mixture
        [4 marks — 1 mark for each correct answer]
   b)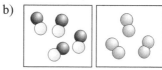

   [1 mark for circling both correct diagrams]
   c) In an element the molecules are made up of one
        type of atom joined together *[1 mark]*, whereas in
        a compound the molecules are made up of different
        types of atoms joined together *[1 mark]*.
2 E.g. sodium and chlorine react to produce the solid and
   chemical reactions between two different elements produce
   compounds *[1 mark]*. The properties of the solid are
   different to those of sodium or chlorine (e.g. the solid can
   be eaten, but chlorine is poisonous) *[1 mark]*.

Page 43 — Chemical Formulae

1 a) NaOH *[1 mark]*
   b) H_2SO_4 *[1 mark]*
2 A: oxygen *[1 mark]*
   B: water *[1 mark]*
   C: calcium carbonate *[1 mark]*
3 a) sodium chloride *[1 mark]*
   b) iron sulfide *[1 mark]*
4 a) CH_4 *[1 mark]*
   b) methane *[1 mark]*

Pages 44-46 — Properties of Metals and Non-Metals

1 a) helium *[1 mark]*

  b) zinc *[1 mark]*

2 Graphite, made from the element carbon, is used in making the 'lead' in pencils. In graphite, the **forces** between the particles are **weak**. Graphite wears away quickly because it's easy to **scrub** atoms off it.
[3 marks — 1 mark for each correct word]

3 a) non-metal *[1 mark]*

  b) malleability *[1 mark]*

  c) It shows substance Q is an electrical insulator *[1 mark]*. This is because the atoms in most non-metals are arranged so that charged particles (electrons) can't move through them *[1 mark]*.

4 a) Samples 1 and 3 *[1 mark]*

  b) Sample 2 *[1 mark]*

  c) An electrical conductor *[1 mark]* because it is a metal and metals contain charged particles (electrons) that are free to move between the atoms and carry electric charge *[1 mark]*.

5 a) E.g. metals are thermal conductors *[1 mark]*. This means they let heat pass through so it can be transferred to the food in the saucepan *[1 mark]*.

  b) E.g. non-metals are thermal insulators *[1 mark]*. This means not much heat is transferred from the pan through the handle *[1 mark]*, so the handle doesn't get too hot to hold *[1 mark]*.

6 a) She will not be able to identify any materials *[1 mark]* because all three of iron, aluminium and graphite can conduct electricity so will have the same result *[1 mark]*.

  b) E.g. take one of the rods and drop beads of melted wax onto one end of it, and wait for the beads of wax to set *[1 mark]*. Put the rod in a clamp stand and use a Bunsen burner to heat the end of the rod where there's no wax *[1 mark]*. Time how long it takes for the beads to fall off (if they do at all) *[1 mark]*, then repeat the experiment with the other rods to see which one loses its beads the fastest and therefore is the best conductor of heat *[1 mark]*.

  c) graphite *[1 mark]*
Non-metals tend to be weak and brittle, so break easily. The only material that is a non-metal is graphite, so rod B must be made of graphite.

  d) Rod A: aluminium
    Rod C: iron
    [1 mark for getting both correct]
Iron is magnetic, whereas aluminium is not, so the rod that is attracted to the bar magnet must be made out of iron.

Section C3 — Purity, Mixtures and Separating Mixtures

Pages 47-48 — Purity and Mixtures

1 a) A pure substance is always made up of **particles of only one element or one compound** *[1 mark]*.

  b) The citric acid isn't pure *[1 mark]*.

2 a) The forces holding the sugar molecules together break *[1 mark]*. The sugar molecules mix with the water molecules to form a solution *[1 mark]*. The sugar molecules are distributed randomly throughout the water *[1 mark]*.

  b) When the sugar dissolves in the water, it creates a mixture — the sugar and the water are not chemically joined up *[1 mark]*. This means it is possible to separate the two using a physical process *[1 mark]*.

  c) Sugar water is a mixture so has some of the properties, in this case the taste, of the sugar *[1 mark]*.

3 a) E.g. add a sample to a test tube and heat it in a beaker of water over a Bunsen burner *[1 mark]*. Use a thermometer to measure the temperature when it starts to melt *[1 mark]*.

  b) Sample C is pure *[1 mark]* because it melts at an exact temperature rather than over a range *[1 mark]*.

  c) Sample B *[1 mark]*. It is not completely pure because the sample melted over a temperature range rather than at a specific point *[1 mark]*.

  d) The melting point of the wax depends on the melting points of the different substances it's made from, so the mixture must be different to the first type of candle wax *[1 mark]*.

Page 49 — Air

1 a) A mixture is a substance made up of two or more different substances which aren't chemically joined *[1 mark]*.

  b) i) oxygen *[1 mark]*
    ii) nitrogen *[1 mark]*
    iii) E.g. argon / carbon dioxide / water vapour *[1 mark]*.
    iv) oxygen *[1 mark]*

2 Mark the starting position of the water on the test tube *[1 mark]*. Wait until the reaction stops, then mark the finishing position of the water *[1 mark]*. Work out the volume of air in the tube at the start and the end, and use the difference to work out the percentage of the starting volume that has been used up *[1 mark]*.

Page 50 — Properties of Water

1 When most substances freeze, their particles get closer together. This makes the substances **more** dense. When water freezes, the particles get further apart. So ice is **less** dense than liquid water. This means that when you freeze water it **increases** in volume. *[1 mark for each correct answer]*

2 a) To make her experiment a fair test. / The volume of water is a control variable *[1 mark]*.

b)

Dish	Type of water	Mass of solid left in dish (g)
1	seawater	1.06
2	tap water	0.03
3	distilled water	0.00

[2 marks for all three correct, or 1 mark for one correct.]

c) No. Although the water is no longer boiling, it can be removed from the dish by evaporation, as this can happen at any temperature *[1 mark]*.

Page 51 — Distillation

1 a) E.g. the inside of the Liebig condenser tube is cold so when the hot gas leaving the flask enters the condenser, it cools and condenses back into liquid water *[1 mark]*.

b) When you turn off the heat, the air in the flask cools and contracts, which could suck liquid back into the flask *[1 mark]*.

c) The colour of the squash would get darker *[1 mark]* because as the water evaporates, the solution in the flask will become more concentrated *[1 mark]*.

Page 52 — Chromatography

1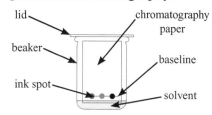

[4 marks for all six labels correct, otherwise 3 marks for any four labels correct, 2 marks for any three labels correct and 1 mark for any two labels correct]

2 a) three *[1 mark]*

b) Pen B *[1 mark]* because it has the same number of spots in the same positions as the sample *[1 mark]*.

c) The substances in the ink in a pen can be separated by the solvent, but pencil marks are not moved by it *[1 mark]*.

Section C4 — Combustion and Thermal Decomposition

Page 53 — Chemical Reactions

1 During a chemical reaction **atoms are rearranged** *[1 mark]*.

2 oxygen + hydrogen → water *[1 mark]*

3 a) Any one from: e.g. the number of bananas in the bunch / the size of the bananas / the variety of the bananas / the ripeness of the bananas before the experiment / the length of time the bananas were left for *[1 mark]*.

b) The bananas kept in the container have more brown spots, so they have ripened more *[1 mark]*. So keeping bananas in a sealed container causes them to ripen faster *[1 mark]*.

Pages 54-55 — More on Reactions and Using Bunsen Burners

1 a) Difference in mass = mass before – mass after
= 40.0 – 39.3 = 0.7 g *[1 mark]*

b) Some mass may have escaped in the form of gas during the reaction *[1 mark]*.

c) Because the total number of each type of atom is the same before and after the reaction *[1 mark]*.
As no atoms are lost or gained, no mass is lost or gained.

d) E.g. repeat the experiment several times and calculate the mean difference in mass *[1 mark]*.

2 a) The air hole should be half-open *[1 mark]*.

b) Closing the air hole of the Bunsen burner **decreases the temperature of the flame because it decreases the amount of air entering the burner** *[1 mark]*.

c) i) yellow *[1 mark]*
ii) Any two from: e.g. put a heat-resistant mat under the burner / tie long hair back / don't wear loose clothing / handle any objects that have been heated with tongs/gloves *[1 mark each for any sensible safety precautions, up to a maximum of 2 marks.]*

d) E.g.

[1 mark for a circle drawn around the top of the inner cone.]

Pages 56-57 — Combustion

1 Combustion is when a substance **burns** in oxygen to release energy.
An example of a combustion reaction is **a bonfire**.
[2 marks — 1 mark for each correct answer.]

2 a) A fuel containing only hydrogen and carbon *[1 mark]*.

b) hydrocarbon + oxygen →
carbon dioxide + **water** (+ energy) *[1 mark]*

3 a) fuel / unburnt wood *[1 mark]*

b) If the glowing splint is held in oxygen, it will relight *[1 mark]*.

4 The limewater will turn cloudy *[1 mark]*.

5 carbon + oxygen → carbon dioxide *[1 mark]*

6 a) The magnesium will burn with a bright flame *[1 mark]*.

b) E.g. she shouldn't look directly at the bright light produced *[1 mark]*.

7 a) sulfur dioxide *[1 mark]*

b) It will burn more brightly in the jar of oxygen compared to in the air *[1 mark]* because air is only about 20% oxygen *[1 mark]*.

Page 58 — The Effects of Fossil Fuels

1 a) Particulates of soot (carbon)/unburnt fuel *[1 mark]* and carbon monoxide *[1 mark]*.

b) If a fuel contains sulfur impurities, sulfur dioxide will be released when the fuel is burnt *[1 mark]*. Sulfur dioxide mixes with clouds to form dilute sulfuric acid which falls as acid rain *[1 mark]*.

2 a) E.g. there was an increase in the amount of carbon dioxide in the atmosphere between 1850 and 2000 *[1 mark]*.

b) E.g. because carbon dioxide traps heat from the Sun in the Earth's atmosphere *[1 mark]* so more carbon dioxide could trap more heat (so the average global temperature would get warmer) *[1 mark]*.

c) Any one from: e.g. reduce the amount of fossil fuels we burn / reduce deforestation / plant more trees *[1 mark]*.

Page 59 — Thermal Decomposition Reactions

1 a) white *[1 mark]*

b) It would change from white to blue *[1 mark]*.

2 a) copper oxide *[1 mark]*

b) carbon dioxide *[1 mark]*

c) copper carbonate → copper oxide + carbon dioxide *[1 mark]*

3 a) calcium oxide *[1 mark]* and carbon dioxide *[1 mark]*

b) e.g. copper oxide *[1 mark]*

Section C5 — Oxidation Reactions, Acids and Alkalis

Page 60 — Reactions of Metals with Oxygen and Water

1 a) A, C, B *[1 mark]*

b) i) hydrogen *[1 mark]*

ii) He should hold a lit splint at the end of the test tube *[1 mark]*. If hydrogen is present this will result in a squeaky pop *[1 mark]*.

c) metal oxide and hydrogen *[1 mark]*

2 a) oxidation *[1 mark]*

b) Most metals react with oxygen to form a metal **oxide.** *[1 mark]*

Page 61 — Oxidation — Rusting

1 a) iron oxide / rust *[1 mark]*

Officially, it's called hydrated iron(III) oxide.

b) rusting / oxidation *[1 mark]*

c) E.g. in one test tube add a nail and cover it with boiled water with a layer of oil on top (to remove oxygen). In another test tube add a nail and half cover it with water. In the final test tube add a nail without any water. *[2 marks for all three test tubes set up correctly, 1 mark for at least one set up correctly]*.

Anan would find that only the nail half covered with water would rust — showing that both oxygen and water are needed for rust to form.

2 a) The iron has reacted with oxygen and water in the air / with water on the ground *[1 mark]*.

b) The oil creates a barrier between the iron chain and oxygen and water *[1 mark]* but still allows the chain to move *[1 mark]*.

c) E.g. painting/coating with plastic / coating with a layer of a different metal / galvanising *[1 mark]*

Page 62 — Acids and Alkalis

1 a) drain cleaner *[1 mark]*

b) E.g. pH 2 (accept any value between 0 and 3) *[1 mark]*

c) E.g. she could add a drop of vinegar to blue litmus paper *[1 mark]*. Acidic solutions will turn blue litmus paper red *[1 mark]*.

2 a) (7.2 + 7.8 + 7.0 + 7.7 + 8.0 + 8.5) ÷ 6 = 46.2 ÷ 6 = 7.7 *[1 mark]*

b) sample site 3 *[1 mark]*

c) blue *[1 mark]*

d) They won't grow well, because the soil is slightly alkaline / the pH is too high *[1 mark]*.

Pages 63-64 — Neutralisation

1 A neutralisation reaction **is a reaction that produces products with a neutral pH** *[1 mark]*.

2 copper sulfate — sulfuric acid *[1 mark]*
magnesium nitrate — nitric acid *[1 mark]*
zinc chloride — hydrochloric acid *[1 mark]*

3 a) green *[1 mark]*

b) water *[1 mark]*

4 a) water *[1 mark]* + carbon dioxide *[1 mark]*

b) calcium carbonate + sulfuric acid:
calcium sulfate *[1 mark]*
sodium carbonate + hydrochloric acid:
sodium chloride *[1 mark]*
magnesium carbonate + nitric acid:
magnesium nitrate *[1 mark]*

5 a) sodium chloride *[1 mark]*

b) E.g. wear eye protection / safety goggles / gloves when handling the solutions *[1 mark]*.

c) His final pH reading is higher than 7 / is alkaline *[1 mark]*. This shows there is leftover/unreacted alkali in the solution as well as the salt, so the sample will not be pure *[1 mark]*.

Page 65 — Reactions of Metals with Acids

1 a)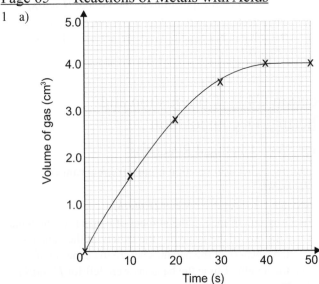

[1 mark for correctly plotted points, 1 mark for curved line of best fit]

b) hydrogen *[1 mark]* and aluminium chloride *[1 mark]*

c) E.g. for each metal, measure the volume of gas produced in a fixed time *[1 mark]*. The most reactive metal will produce the most gas *[1 mark]*.
Alternatively, you could have said to measure the time taken to produce a fixed volume of gas for each metal — the most reactive metal would have taken the least amount of time.

Page 66 — Reactions of Oxides with Acids

1 **sodium hydroxide solution (pH 14)** *[1 mark]*
2 a) Metal oxides have a pH which is **higher** than 7 so they are **alkaline** *[1 mark]*.
  b) salt and water *[1 mark]*.
  c) The metal oxide solution *[1 mark]*.
3 a) magnesium + oxygen → magnesium oxide *[1 mark]*
  b) A pH higher than 7 *[1 mark]*.
  c) i) neutralisation *[1 mark]*.
     ii) magnesium sulfate *[1 mark]*

Page 67 — Limestone

1 a) calcium carbonate *[1 mark]*
  b) i) It can be damaged by acid rain *[1 mark]*.
     ii) Any two from: e.g. making cement / making mortar / making concrete / making glass *[2 marks — 1 mark for each correct answer]*
  c) calcium chloride *[1 mark]*, water *[1 mark]* and carbon dioxide *[1 mark]*
2 a) i) It increases soil pH *[1 mark]*.
     ii) neutralisation reaction *[1 mark]*
  b) Limestone is heated to produce calcium oxide (and carbon dioxide) *[1 mark]*. Water is then added to the calcium oxide to make agricultural lime *[1 mark]*.

Page 68 — Acids and the Environment

1 a) carbon dioxide *[1 mark]*
  b) e.g. sulfur dioxide *[1 mark]*
  c) Both statues will be damaged by acid rain *[1 mark]*. Limestone contains calcium carbonate, which will react with the acids, undergoing chemical weathering *[1 mark]*. Magnesium will react with the acids and corrode *[1 mark]*.
2 a) chemical weathering *[1 mark]*
  b) E.g. large cities produce more of the gases that form acid rain / large cities produce more pollution *[1 mark]*.

Section P1 — Energy Transfers and Resources

Pages 69-70 — Energy Stores and Energy Transfers

1 a) chemical *[1 mark]*
  b) elastic *[1 mark]*
  c) nuclear *[1 mark]*
2 a) by mechanical work *[1 mark]*
  b) by heating *[1 mark]*
3 a) gravitational potential energy store *[1 mark]*
  b) kinetic energy store *[1 mark]*
  c) E.g. by sound *[1 mark]*

4 a) Energy is transferred from the **internal** energy store of the cup of tea to the **internal** energy store of Louis' hand. Whilst this is happening, the cup of tea will **cool down** and Louis' hand will **warm up**. The temperature difference between the cup of tea and Louis' hand **decreases** over time. *[5 marks available — 1 mark for each correct answer]*
  b)

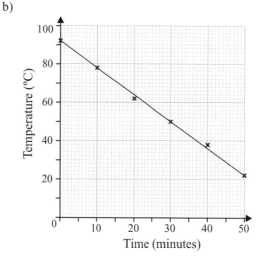

[1 mark for correctly drawn line of best fit]
  c) 72 °C (accept any answer between 70 °C and 74 °C) *[1 mark]*
You should have worked this out from the graph by drawing a vertical line up from 14 minutes on the x-axis to your line of best fit, and then a horizontal line across from here to the y-axis. Where this line crosses the y-axis gives you your answer.

Page 71 — Conservation of Energy

1 a) False *[1 mark]*
  b) True *[1 mark]*
2 24 000 J *[1 mark]*
The total input is equal to the total output, which is 20 400 + 3600 = 24 000 J.

3 Because energy can't be created, it can only be transferred from one store to another *[1 mark]*.
4 a) the car's kinetic energy store *[1 mark]*
  b) Energy is lost to the environment by heating and sound *[1 mark]*.
  c) total energy input = the useful energy + the wasted energy
    the wasted energy = total energy input – the useful energy
    = 60 – 20
    = 40 J *[1 mark]*

Page 72 — Fossil Fuels and Energy Resources

1 plants *[1 mark]*
2 a) E.g. coal, oil and gas *[1 mark]*.
  b) Energy from the **Sun** is absorbed by plants during **photosynthesis**. Creatures can **take in** this energy by eating the plants. Some of this energy is **stored** in the tissues of both the plants and animals. When plants and animals die they can become buried and slowly decay, and over **millions of years** the pressure can turn these remains into **fossil fuels**. *[6 marks available — 1 mark for each correct answer]*
  c) By burning them *[1 mark]*.

Page 73 — Generating Electricity and More on Fossil Fuels

1 Coal is burnt in a boiler, which releases energy *[1 mark]*. This is used to heat up water which then changes to high pressure steam *[1 mark]*. The energy in the internal energy store of the steam is transferred to the kinetic energy store of the turbine *[1 mark]*. The turbine is attached to a generator, which spins and generates electricity *[1 mark]*.

2 a) E.g. burnt in fireplaces to heat homes / to power steam trains *[1 mark]*

  b) E.g. to make petrol and diesel which are used as fuel in cars *[1 mark]*

  c) E.g. in boilers to heat homes / in ovens and hobs for cooking *[1 mark]*

Page 74 — More on Generating Electricity

1 Electricity is generated from wave power by **waves pushing air in and out of a turbine**. *[1 mark]*

2 a) E.g. wood *[1 mark]*

  b) E.g. wind power / wave power / hydroelectric power / solar power / geothermal power / tidal power *[2 marks available — 1 mark for each correct answer]*.

3 The arrows labelled by *x* represent cold water being pumped down towards the hot rocks *[1 mark]*. The arrows labelled by *y* represent the steam (that this cold water turns into when it reaches the hot rocks), rising back up to the surface *[1 mark]*.

Page 75 — Renewable and Non-Renewable Energy Resources

1 a) Non-renewable energy resources can't be replaced in a person's lifetime, whereas renewable energy resources can *[1 mark]*.

  b) Any two from: e.g. coal/oil/gas/nuclear fuel *[2 marks available — 1 mark for each correct answer]*

  c) Any three from: e.g. biomass/wind/wave/solar/ hydroelectric/tidal/geothermal *[3 marks available — 1 mark for each correct answer]*

2 a) Any two from: e.g. solar power is a renewable resource and so won't run out, but coal could run out as it is non-renewable. / If more solar power is used, less coal will be used, which means the coal won't run out as quickly. / Using more solar power and less coal will reduce the overall amount of pollutants released whilst electricity is being generated. / Carbon dioxide and sulfur dioxide released from burning coal can lead to global warming and acid rain whereas solar power doesn't release either of these gases. / Light from the Sun is free, but coal costs money, so it will be cheaper for the country once the solar panels are up and running. *[2 marks available — 1 mark for each correct answer]*

  b) Any two from: e.g. it would cost a lot of money for the government to build the solar panels. / Solar panels don't produce as much energy as a coal-fired power station, so the government would need to build a lot of solar panels to get a substantial amount of energy. / Solar panels depend on the amount of sunlight, so are not as reliable as coal. / Although burning coal damages the environment, the initial set-up of the solar panels would also cause some damage to the environment, whereas the coal-fired power station already exists. *[2 marks available — 1 mark for each correct answer]*

Section P2 — Speed and Forces

Page 76 — Speed

1 speed = distance ÷ time
  = 6600 ÷ 12
  = 550 mph

[2 marks for correct answer, otherwise 1 mark for correct formula.]

2 a) speed = distance ÷ time
  = 900 ÷ 1000
  = 0.9 m/s

[2 marks for correct answer, otherwise 1 mark for correct formula.]

  b) speed = distance ÷ time ⇒ time = distance ÷ speed
  time = 10 ÷ 40 = 0.25 hours

[2 marks for correct answer, otherwise 1 mark for correct rearrangement of formula.]

3 a) 50 cm = 0.5 m
  speed = distance ÷ time
  = 0.5 ÷ 5
  = 0.1 m/s

[3 marks for correct answer, otherwise 1 mark for correct conversion of cm to m, and 1 mark for correct formula.]

  b) speed = distance ÷ time ⇒ time = distance ÷ speed
  time = 0.5 ÷ 2.5 = 0.2 seconds

[2 marks for correct answer, otherwise 1 mark for correct rearrangement of formula.]

Pages 77-78 — More on Speed

1 Relative speed = speed of car – speed of bus
  = 73 – 56 = 17 mph *[1 mark]*

2 Relative speed = speed of train A + speed of train B
  = 30 + 45 = 75 mph *[1 mark]*

3 a) E.g. record the time taken for each horse to run the length of the track *[1 mark]*. Divide the length of the track by each time taken to get the speed of each horse *[1 mark]*.

  b) Repeat the test multiple times and check she gets the same/very similar results each time *[1 mark]*.

  c) Any one from: e.g. make sure the weather conditions are similar for both horses / get both horses to run on the same track / have the same start and end positions for both horses / make sure both horses have had the same amount of food/rest before the run *[1 mark]*.

4　a)　E.g. a stopwatch / a measuring tape *[1 mark]*
　b)　E.g. to reduce the effect of random errors / to make the results more reliable / to make the results more accurate *[1 mark]*.
　c)　Runner 1 *[1 mark]*
　d)　speed = distance ÷ time
　　　　　= 100 ÷ 12.5 = 8 m/s
　　　[2 marks for correct answer, otherwise 1 mark for correct formula.]
　e)　i)　Runner 3 *[1 mark]*
　　　ii)　Mean time = (11.5 + 12.0 + 12.5) ÷ 3
　　　　　　　　　= 12.0 s *[1 mark]*

Page 79 — Stopping Distances

1　a)　a wet road *[1 mark]*
　b)　braking distance = stopping distance – thinking distance
　　　　　　　= 74 – 16 = 58 m
　　　[2 marks for correct answer, otherwise 1 mark for correct formula.]
　c)　Car B *[1 mark]* because it had the greatest stopping distance *[1 mark]*.
　d)　Any two from: e.g. tiredness of the driver / whether the driver is under the influence of alcohol/drugs / attitude of the driver / weather conditions *[2 marks]*.

Page 80 — Forces

1　a)　It is a push or a pull that occurs when two objects interact *[1 mark]*.
　b)　Forces are measured in units called **newtons** *[1 mark]*.
　c)　Any two from: e.g. slow down / stop moving / change direction / turn / change shape *[2 marks]*
　d)　The direction of the arrow shows the direction of the force *[1 mark]* and the length of the arrow shows the size of the force *[1 mark]*.
2　It will slow down the car *[1 mark]*.
3

force from engine

[1 mark for drawing an arrow of equal length, 1 mark for drawing the arrow pointing backwards.]

Pages 81-82 — Balanced and Unbalanced Forces

1　B and D *[1 mark]*
2　a)　speeding up *[1 mark]*
　b)　moving upwards at an increasing speed *[1 mark]*
3

Scenario	Balanced	Unbalanced
A cyclist starting off.	✗	✓
A car slowing down.	✗	✓
A model trolley travelling down a slope.	✗	✓
A marathon runner going at a steady speed along a straight road.	✓	✗

[2 marks for all correct, otherwise 1 mark for at least two correct.]

4　a)　The cherry will stay on top of the frosting *[1 mark]*.
　b)　The cherry will sink into the frosting *[1 mark]*.
5　a)　The forces are unbalanced because the overall backwards force is greater than the forward force *[1 mark]*.
　　　Overall horizontal force = 6000 – (7000 + 1000)
　　　　　　　　　　= –2000 N
　b)　The car moves at a constant speed *[1 mark]*.

Pages 83-84 — Friction and Air Resistance

1　a)　Friction is a force between two surfaces that makes it harder for objects to slide past each other *[1 mark]*.
　b)　i)　E.g. it allows the skater to grip the ice to steer and control his/her movement / it allows the skater to stop *[1 mark]*.
　　　ii)　E.g. it wastes the skater's energy / it limits the skater's top speed *[1 mark]*.
2　a)　Air resistance is a force that pushes against objects moving through the air *[1 mark]*.
　b)　Because the skydiver only has the force of gravity/her weight pulling her down (air resistance hasn't started to act) *[1 mark]*.
　c)　i)　It increases *[1 mark]*.
　　　ii)　The air resistance becomes equal to the skydiver's weight so the forces are balanced *[1 mark]*.
3　a)　Any four from: cut different sizes of square canopies out of the plastic *[1 mark]*. Mark the point above the ground that the weight will be dropped from and hold the parachute and weight at the fixed height *[1 mark]*. Get someone to start a stopwatch when the weight is released and stop it when the weight touches the ground *[1 mark]*. Record the time taken for the weight to hit the ground *[1 mark]*. Repeat the procedure for each canopy area *[1 mark]*.
　　　[A maximum of four marks available]
　b)　Any two from: e.g. the mass/size of the weight / the method of attaching the weight to the parachute / the shape of the parachute / the plastic the parachute is made from / the weather conditions *[2 marks]*.
　c)　To make sure her results are reliable/repeatable *[1 mark]*.
　d)　E.g. to help the parachute keep its shape / to stop the parachute from being blown off course *[1 mark]*.
　e)　Increasing the area of the parachute's canopy increases the air resistance that acts on it *[1 mark]*, so the bigger the area of the parachute's canopy, the slower it will fall *[1 mark]*.

Page 85 — Springs

1　a)　He would set up the spring next to a ruler *[1 mark]* then find the difference between the length of the spring before and after the weight is added *[1 mark]*.
　b)　i)　The weight placed on top of the spring *[1 mark]*.
　　　ii)　The compression of the spring *[1 mark]*.
　c)　Mean = (3.6 + 3.9 + 3.6) ÷ 3
　　　　　= 3.7 cm *[1 mark]*
　d)　The 0.2 N weight *[1 mark]*. The three readings are the closest to the mean / the least spread out *[1 mark]*.
　e)　E.g. as the weight on the spring increases, the compression of the spring increases / compression and force are directly proportional *[1 mark]*.

Section P3 — Pressure and Density

Pages 86-87 — Pressure

1   Pressure is calculated using **force divided by area**. The greater the area over which the force acts, the **smaller** the pressure. *[1 mark]*

2   a)   pressure = force ÷ area = 0.20 ÷ 2.5 = 0.08 N/cm²
    [2 marks for correct answer, otherwise 1 mark for correct formula.]

    b)   pressure = force ÷ area
    ⇒ area = force ÷ pressure = 0.20 ÷ 0.4 = 0.5 cm²
    [2 marks for correct answer, otherwise 1 mark for correct rearrangement of formula.]

3   Snowshoes increase the area over which the force of a person's weight is applied *[1 mark]*. Pressure = force ÷ area, so the pressure on the ground due to the person's weight decreases *[1 mark]*, so the person will not sink into the snow as much when walking *[1 mark]*.

4   a)   The thickness of the wood *[1 mark]*.

    b)   They can calculate the pressure by dividing the weight of the sand by the area of the bags in contact with the wood *[1 mark]*.

    c)   If the wood breaks it could be dangerous/unsafe for humans stood on it *[1 mark]*.

    d)   E.g. the area of a person's feet is smaller than the area of the bags in contact with the wood *[1 mark]*, so the pressure due to a standing person will be greater than the bags of sand *[1 mark]*.

5   An individual nail point has a small area and so a large pressure results which causes the balloon to pop *[1 mark]*. For a bed of nails, the nails together provide a larger area to distribute the weight of the balloon *[1 mark]*. This means the pressure exerted on the balloon from each nail is much lower than when using one nail, so the nails don't pop the balloon *[1 mark]*.

Pages 88-89 — Density

1   a)   density = mass ÷ volume *[1 mark]*

    b)   i)   Volume = length × width × height
            = 1.2 × 0.6 × 2.0 = 1.44 cm³ *[1 mark]*

        ii)   density = mass ÷ volume
        ⇒ mass = density × volume
        mass = 2.5 × 1.44 = 3.6 g
        [2 marks for correct answer, otherwise 1 mark for correct rearrangement of formula.]

    c)   The actual mass of the pendant will be lower because the estimated volume is larger than the actual volume of the pendant *[1 mark]*.
    The estimated volume didn't account for the rounded corners that don't fill the volume of a cuboid.

    d)   E.g. pour water from the jug into the measuring cylinder so that it is partly filled, and measure the volume of the water *[1 mark]*. Lower the pendant into the water so that it is submerged, and measure the new level of the water *[1 mark]*. The volume of the pendant is equal to the change in level of the water *[1 mark]*.

2   He should measure the mass of an empty beaker, then pour the liquid in and measure the mass of the beaker and liquid *[1 mark]*. He should then work out the change in mass, which is equal to the mass of the liquid *[1 mark]*. He should find the volume of the liquid by reading off the scale *[1 mark]*. He can then calculate the density using density = mass ÷ volume *[1 mark]*.

3   a)   volume of spoon
        = volume of water and spoon − volume of water
        = 255.0 − 250.0 = 5.0 cm³ *[1 mark]*

    b)   Density = mass ÷ volume = 45 ÷ 5.0
                = 9.0 g/cm³ *[1 mark]*
    The density of the spoon is closest to the density of the copper, so the spoon is most likely to be made from copper *[1 mark]*.
    You'll still get the mark for part b) if the answer you used from part a) was wrong.

Page 90 — More on Density

1   a)   Liquids that don't mix together. *[1 mark]*

    b)   E.g. the experiment shows that a liquid with a lower density will float on a liquid with a higher density *[1 mark]*.

2   Beaker: B *[1 mark]*
Explanation: The particles in the warm water will be further apart from each other than the particles in the cold water *[1 mark]*. This means that the warm water will have a lower density than the cold water, so the warm water will float on top of the cold water *[1 mark]*.

3   Any four points from: e.g. Find the mass of the deflated balloon, then blow up the balloon and find the mass again *[1 mark]*. Work out the change in mass, which is the mass of the air inside the balloon *[1 mark]*. Put some water in a container and record the water level, then push the balloon into the container and record the water level again *[1 mark]*. Work out the change in water level, which is roughly equal to the volume of air inside the balloon *[1 mark]*. Then calculate the density using density = mass ÷ volume *[1 mark]*. *[Maximum of 4 marks available]*.

Section P4 — Sound and Light

Page 91 — Sound

1   A sound wave is a wave of vibrating **particles** which are produced by a **vibrating** object. In order to travel, sound waves require a **medium**. Whilst sound can't travel through a **vacuum** it can travel through **solids**, liquids and air. In different mediums sound has a **finite** speed.
[6 marks — 1 mark for each correct answer]

2   a)   E.g. sound travels faster through solids than gases *[1 mark]*, so the sound waves travelled faster through the ground and reached Russell sooner than the sound waves travelling through the air *[1 mark]*.

    b)   (75 + 75 + 100) ÷ 0.71 = 352.1 m/s *[2 marks — 1 mark for correct method and 1 mark for correct answer]*

Page 92 — More on Sound

1 a) i) The number of complete waves that pass a point in one second *[1 mark]*.

 ii) The higher the frequency of a noise, the higher pitched it is *[1 mark]*.

If you write this the other way round (the lower the frequency, the lower the pitch) that's fine.

 b) i) road drill *[1 mark]*

 ii) scream *[1 mark]*

The scream has the greatest amplitude, so it is the loudest sound.

2 a) i) true *[1 mark]*

 ii) false *[1 mark]*

 iii) true *[1 mark]*

 b) Measure the height of the sound wave *[1 mark]*.

 c) To prevent damage to their hearing *[1 mark]*.

Page 93 — Hearing

1 a) It is the range of frequencies (vibrations per second) that an animal/human can hear *[1 mark]*.

 b) i) cat *[1 mark]*

 ii) shark *[1 mark]*

2 a) E.g. Matthew could start by playing sounds with frequencies as low as 20 Hz *[1 mark]*. Then he could play sounds of gradually increasing frequency until the person can no longer hear a sound so no longer raises their hand *[1 mark]*.

 b) Any two from: e.g. the loudspeaker should be set at the same volume *[1 mark]*. / They should be sat at the same distance from the loudspeaker *[1 mark]*. / The changes in frequency should be the same size *[1 mark]*. / They should have the same number of attempts at hearing a frequency *[1 mark]*.

 c) His grandparents *[1 mark]* because as you get older your ability to hear high frequency sounds decreases *[1 mark]*.

Pages 94-95 — Light

1 a) The pinhole needs to be small so that **only one ray from each point on the object gets into the camera**. *[1 mark]*

 b) i) E.g.

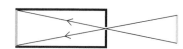

 [1 mark for drawing two lines from the object through the pinhole to the paper, 1 mark for drawing arrows pointing in the correct direction.]

 ii) The image will be upside down and crossed over/ flipped *[1 mark]* because the rays of light cross over as they pass through the pinhole *[1 mark]*.

2 a) Light waves travel **in a straight line** *[1 mark]*.

 b) Light waves travel fastest in a **vacuum** *[1 mark]*.

3 a) Light travels so fast that the light will reach the sensor almost instantly *[1 mark]*. The sensor can only measure to the nearest hundredth of a second, so it will not be able to measure the tiny amount of time light takes to travel 30 m *[1 mark]*.

 b) Jacques would hear the gun after seeing it fire, as light travels faster than sound *[1 mark]*.

 c) Light waves don't need particles to travel, but sound waves do *[1 mark]*. There aren't any particles in a vacuum so sound waves can't travel through it, but light can *[1 mark]*.

Page 96 — Reflection

1 a)

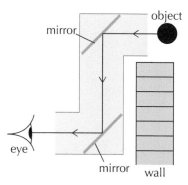

 [1 mark for straight lines with correct arrows from object to eye and 1 mark for angle of incidence and reflection equal at each mirror]

 b)

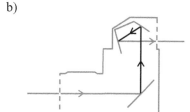

 [1 mark for straight lines with correct arrows and 1 mark for angle of incidence and reflection equal at each mirror]

2 It is not able to see the falcon's reflection. Since angle of incidence = angle of reflection *[1 mark]*, the light rays from the falcon are reflected to the opposite side of the puddle to the prairie dog *[1 mark]*.

Page 97 — Refraction

1 a) When the light passes from the water to the air at an angle to the normal it changes **direction**. This is known as **refraction**. *[1 mark]*

 b) As the light travels from a more dense medium to a less dense medium, it bends **away from** the normal. *[1 mark]*

c) i)

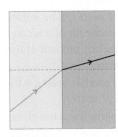

[1 mark]

ii)

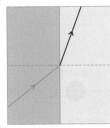

[1 mark]

iii)

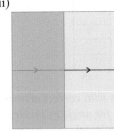

[1 mark]

d)

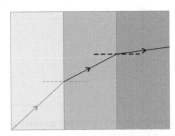

[2 marks — 1 mark for each correct ray drawn]
Angles don't need to be exactly the same as the examples here — marks to be awarded as long as the ray bends in the right direction compared to the normal.

Page 98 — Light and Materials

1 a) dispersion *[1 mark]*
   b) red *[1 mark]*
   c) White light is made up of different colours *[1 mark]*. Different colours have different frequencies *[1 mark]*. Different frequencies are refracted by different amounts *[1 mark]*.
   d) transparent *[1 mark]*
   e) E.g. in a rainbow *[1 mark]*, different colours are refracted by different amounts in raindrops *[1 mark]*.

Section P5 — Circuits and Magnets

Page 99 — Electrical Circuits

1 a) The more cells there are in a circuit, the **higher** the current *[1 mark]*.
       Current **is not** used up as it flows around a circuit *[1 mark]*.

b) Insulating material has a very high resistance *[1 mark]*. This will reduce the current, so the bulb will not light *[1 mark]*.

2

Material	Current (A)	Resistance (Ω)	Conductor or insulator?
A	0.00024	1.06	insulator
B	16	0.03	conductor
C	10	0.00	conductor

[4 marks available — 1 mark for each correct answer]
The current of material A is much lower than the current of material C, so the resistance of material A must be higher, meaning it has the higher of the two values (1.06 Ω). As material A has a high resistance it is an insulator, whereas material C has a low resistance, so is a conductor.

Pages 100-101 — More on Electrical Circuits

1 a) an SPST *[1 mark]*
   b) A resistor **reduces current** *[1 mark]*.
   c) A variable resistor **gives control over reduction in current** *[1 mark]*.

2

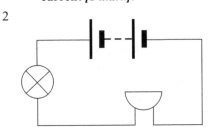

[3 marks available — 1 mark for correctly drawing the battery, 1 mark for correctly drawing the bulb and 1 mark for correctly drawing the buzzer.]

3 a) light emitting diode / LED *[1 mark]*
   b) i) ampere / amp *[1 mark]*
       ii) ammeter *[1 mark]*
   c) a fuse *[1 mark]*

4 a)

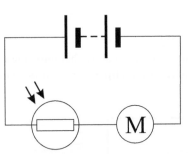

[2 marks available — 1 mark for correctly drawing a motor and 1 mark for correctly drawing a light dependent resistor.]

b) The intensity of light shone on the light dependent resistor *[1 mark]*.

Page 102 — Series Circuits

1 a) E.g. they are in series because the current has no choice but to pass through them both *[1 mark]*.
   b) There is no current/0 A passing through A_2. The branch of the circuit containing A_2 is broken by the open switch, so no current can pass through *[1 mark]*.
   c) The current will increase *[1 mark]*.

2   Removing the motor from the circuit will **decrease** the resistance in the circuit. This will **increase** the current flowing. The current measured will be **the same** at any point in the circuit *[3 marks available — 1 mark for each correct answer]*.

Page 103 — Parallel Circuits

1 a) Bulbs 2 and 3 *[1 mark]*
   b) Bulb 1 *[1 mark]*

2

Ammeter	A_1	A_2	A_3	A_4	A_5
Reading (A)	9.2	3.9	2.6	2.7	9.2

[2 marks available — 1 mark for each correct answer]
The current at A_5 is equal to the current at A_1. The current of A_2, A_3 and A_4 must all add up to the current at A_1, so:
$A_4 = A_1 - A_2 - A_3 = 9.2 - 3.9 - 2.6 = 2.7$ A

3

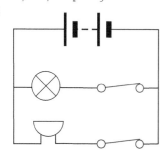

[4 marks available — 1 mark for correctly drawing the bulb and buzzer, 1 mark for correctly drawing the battery, 1 mark for drawing the bulb and buzzer in parallel with one another and 1 mark for drawing switches on each branch of the circuit.]

Pages 104-105 — Magnets

1 a)

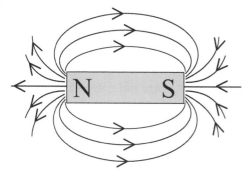

[2 marks available — 1 mark for correctly drawn field lines and 1 mark for field line arrows pointing from the North pole to the South pole.]

   b) The closer the field lines are to each other, the stronger the magnetic field at that point *[1 mark]*.
   c) If you put a compass near a magnet, the needle will align itself with the magnet's magnetic field *[1 mark]*.

2 a) Only one of the blocks is a magnet *[1 mark]*.
If they were both magnets, they would repel each other in one of the two positions shown.
   b) By holding each block next to a known magnet in different orientations *[1 mark]*. If a block is repelled, it is a magnet *[1 mark]*.

3 a) E.g. the paperclip / the incline of the surface / the type of surface / the distance she starts from / the person doing the experiment *[1 mark]*.
   b) A systematic error *[1 mark]*.

c)

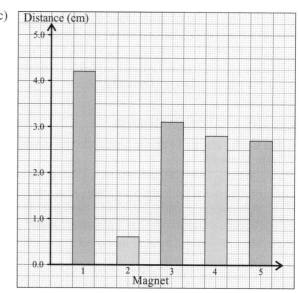

[4 marks available — 1 mark for drawing a bar chart, 1 mark for using a sensible scale, 1 mark for correctly labelled axes, 1 mark for drawing bars accurately.]

Page 106 — Electromagnets

1 a) Wrap the wire in a coil around the iron bar *[1 mark]* and connect the ends of the wire to a power supply so that current is running through the wire *[1 mark]*.
   b) Bar magnets always have a magnetic field (you can't turn it off), electromagnets can have their magnetic field turned off *[1 mark]*.
   c) E.g. supply more current to the wire *[1 mark]* and add more turns to the coil *[1 mark]*.
   d) Scatter iron filings around an electromagnet and they will align along the magnetic field lines of the electromagnet *[1 mark]*.

2 a) When the input circuit is switched on, the electromagnet's field is turned on *[1 mark]*. This causes the iron lever to be attracted to it, causing it to rotate *[1 mark]*. As it rotates the other end of the lever pushes the contacts together, which turns on the output circuit *[1 mark]*.
   b) E.g. in lifting magnets *[1 mark]*

Section P6 — Space

Page 107 — Gravity

1 a) The gravitational attraction between the mass of the Earth and the disc / the Earth's gravitational pull *[1 mark]*.
   b) weight = **mass × gravitational field strength** *[1 mark]*
   c) weight = mass × gravitational field strength
     ⇒ mass = weight ÷ gravitational field strength
     weight of disc = 4 N
     so mass = 4 ÷ 10 = 0.4 kg
[3 marks for the correct answer, otherwise 1 mark for correct rearrangement of formula and 1 mark for reading correct weight from the newton meter.]
   d) weight = mass × gravitational field strength
            = 0.4 × 3.7 = 1.48 N
[2 marks for correct answer, otherwise 1 mark for using answer to c) as the mass.]

2   weight = mass × gravitational field strength
    ⇒ gravitational field strength = weight ÷ mass
    so gravitational field strength = 128 ÷ 80 = 1.6 N/kg
    [2 marks for the correct answer, otherwise 1 mark for correct rearrangement of formula.]

Page 108 — The Solar System

1   The Earth's gravity keeps the Moon orbiting around the Earth *[1 mark]*.

2   a)   Similarity: e.g. both systems have a star at the centre. / Both systems are in the Milky Way. *[1 mark]* Difference: e.g. our Solar System has 8 planets but Proxima Centauri only has 2 planets. *[1 mark]*

    b)   The gravitational force *[1 mark]* between the Sun and the planets *[1 mark]*.

    c)   i)   365¼ days *[1 mark]*
         ii) Uranus *[1 mark]* because it is the furthest from the Sun *[1 mark]*.

    d)   E.g. a moon orbiting a planet / an artificial satellite orbiting the Earth *[1 mark]*.

Pages 109-110 — The Movement of the Earth

1   a)   Because the Earth is rotating around its axis *[1 mark]*.

    b)   The other stars appear to move because the Earth rotates about its axis *[1 mark]*. The Pole Star must therefore be directly above the Earth's axis of rotation *[1 mark]*.

2   a)   During a total eclipse all of the Sun's light is blocked, but during a partial eclipse only some of the Sun's light is blocked *[1 mark]*.

    b)   i)

         [1 mark for drawing the Sun to the left of the Earth]
         ii) The Moon is seen from sunlight reflected off its surface *[1 mark]*. The Earth blocks this light during an eclipse, so the Moon is less bright when viewed from Earth *[1 mark]*.

3   a)   i)   Japan *[1 mark]*
         ii) The Earth completes half a rotation about its axis over 12 hours *[1 mark]*. So Japan will now be facing towards the Sun *[1 mark]*.

    b)   New York is tilted towards the Sun and Argentina is tilted away from the Sun in June *[1 mark]*. This means New York has longer days than Argentina, so New York has more hours of sunshine and more time to heat up *[1 mark]*. The Sun's rays are spread over a smaller area in the northern hemisphere than the southern hemisphere in June, so the heat is more focused in New York than in Argentina *[1 mark]*.

    c)   The Sun reaches a higher point in the sky in summer than in winter *[1 mark]*.

Page 111 — Satellites

1   A probe is **an unmanned spacecraft** *[1 mark]*.

2   a)   E.g. they can carry telescopes to get a clearer look at space without the Earth's atmosphere getting in the way *[1 mark]*.

    b)   E.g. they could be used to find out about weather conditions before/during the trip / to view the Earth from above in order to map the island's location/terrain / to communicate with other scientists in the team / to use GPS on their journey *[1 mark]*.

3   a)   E.g. it's cheaper and safer than sending astronauts into space *[1 mark]*.

    b)   E.g. what conditions are like on Mars *[1 mark]*.

Page 112 — Biology Practice Paper

1   a)   releases energy from food *[1 mark]*
    b)   stigma *[1 mark]*
    c)   an amphibian *[1 mark]*
    d)   starch *[1 mark]*
    e)   carbon dioxide available decreases *[1 mark]*
    f)   animal kingdom *[1 mark]*
    g)   feathery stigmas *[1 mark]*

2   a)   During the menstrual cycle, an egg is released from **an ovary** *[1 mark]*. It then travels along **a fallopian tube** *[1 mark]* to the womb. If the egg has not been fertilised before it reaches the womb, then the lining of **the womb** *[1 mark]* breaks down.

    b)   The testes make sperm *[1 mark]*, which are needed to fertilise an egg cell during reproduction *[1 mark]*.

    c)   the womb/uterus *[1 mark]*

3   a)   From top to bottom: cell surface membrane *[1 mark]*, nucleus *[1 mark]*.

    b)   All of the structures within an animal cell are surrounded by a jelly-like substance called **cytoplasm**. *[1 mark]*

    c)   a tissue *[1 mark]*

    d)   magnification = image size ÷ real size,
         so real size = image size ÷ magnification
         7.5 ÷ 1500 = 0.005 cm *[2 marks for correct answer, otherwise 1 mark for correct rearrangement of formula.]*

4   a)   It helps food move through your digestive system / prevents constipation *[1 mark]*.

    b)   Brand B *[1 mark]* because, e.g. it's lower in fat / higher in fibre / higher in protein *[1 mark]*.

    c)   E.g. Brand A crisps will increase the temperature of the water more than Brand B crisps *[1 mark]*.
         Brand A crisps contain more energy, so should release more energy when burnt, thus giving more energy to the water.

    d)   Any two from: e.g. the mass of each type of crisp / the amount of water in the boiling tube / the distance between the burning crisps and the boiling tube.
         [2 marks — 1 mark for each correct answer.]

    e)   E.g. wear goggles / point the test tube away from herself / stand a safe distance away / place the dish on a heat-proof mat. *[1 mark]*

    f)   Brand A: temperature change = 50 − 22 = 28 °C
         Brand B: temperature change = 43 − 19 = 24 °C
         [1 mark]

g) Repeat the experiment (at least) three times and calculate a mean *[1 mark]*.

h) E.g. she could insulate the apparatus / use a wider-bottomed container for the water *[1 mark]*.

5 a) i) E.g. there are fewer snails for the thrushes to eat *[1 mark]*.

ii) E.g. there are fewer snails to eat the cabbages, so there is more food available for the butterflies / there are fewer thrushes to eat the butterflies *[1 mark]*.

b) E.g. it might have decreased because there are fewer snails for the toads to eat / there are fewer snails for the hedgehogs to eat so they might eat more toads *[1 mark]*.

c) The cabbage provides food for the snails and butterflies, which the thrush then eats so it can survive *[1 mark]*. The thrush eats the consumers of the cabbage, so fewer consumers means more cabbages *[1 mark]*.

d) E.g. place a quadrat on the ground at a random point within the garden *[1 mark]*. Count how many snails are within the quadrat and record the result *[1 mark]*. Repeat as many times as possible *[1 mark]* then work out the mean number of snails per m² and multiply that by the total area of the garden *[1 mark]*.

e) i) He is not correct, because the results are randomly distributed / there is no clear pattern/relationship shown by the graph *[1 mark]*.

ii) E.g. he could increase his sample size *[1 mark]* and choose his sample sites at random (rather than just sampling gardens along his street) *[1 mark]*.

6 a)

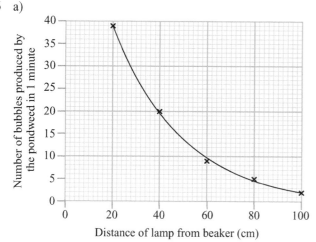

[3 marks — 2 mark for all points plotted correctly, otherwise 1 mark for 4 points plotted correctly; 1 mark for a smooth curve of best fit.]

b) E.g. the amount of gas/oxygen produced in one minute is lower the further the lamp is from the plant / the lower the light intensity is *[1 mark]*.

c) E.g. measure the amount of gas produced with an upturned measuring cylinder/gas syringe *[1 mark]*.
This is more accurate than counting bubbles, as the volume of each gas bubble may vary.

d) The scientist should vary the amount of sodium bicarbonate added to the water and keep the lamp at a constant distance *[1 mark]*.

7 a) The limewater will turn cloudy *[1 mark]* because the woodlice are producing carbon dioxide (a product of aerobic respiration) *[1 mark]*.

b) E.g. anaerobic respiration is less efficient than aerobic respiration. / Anaerobic respiration releases less energy per molecule of glucose than aerobic respiration. / Anaerobic respiration produces lactic acid, which can be painful, whereas aerobic respiration doesn't. *[1 mark]*

c) **glucose → lactic acid** (+ some energy) *[1 mark]*

d) i) The amount of oxygen used by the body increased *[1 mark]*.

ii) In the final two minutes of exercise, the amount of oxygen used remained the same *[1 mark]*. This suggests that the man's muscles were respiring anaerobically (as well as aerobically) to supply the extra energy needed for his muscles to continue to work harder, as this process doesn't require oxygen *[1 mark]*.

8 a) It contracts and moves down *[1 mark]*.

b) Nicotine is a drug used for enjoyment (rather than as medicine/to improve health in some way) *[1 mark]*.

c) Nicotine is an addictive drug *[1 mark]*.

d) When alveoli are destroyed the surface area available for gas exchange is reduced *[1 mark]*. This means that less oxygen is able to diffuse from the alveoli into the blood in each breath *[1 mark]*, so the person needs to breathe more rapidly to get all the oxygen they need *[1 mark]*.

Page 125 — Chemistry Practice Paper

1 a) HCl *[1 mark]*

b) 21% *[1 mark]*

c) A and D *[1 mark]*

d) a salt, water and carbon dioxide *[1 mark]*

e) freezing *[1 mark]*

f) a compound *[1 mark]*

g) sulfur *[1 mark]*

2 a) Fe *[1 mark]*

b) That both air and water must be present in order for iron to rust *[1 mark]*.

c) Nail B will not rust/change appearance *[1 mark]*, because the magnesium will react with the water and air instead of the iron *[1 mark]*.

d) E.g. repeat the experiment with a nail in air and water and another nail in air and salt water *[1 mark]*. Compare the appearance of each nail during the week — whichever one changes appearance more quickly is rusting faster *[1 mark]*.

3 a)

[1 mark]

b) i) subliming *[1 mark]*

ii) The iodine particles gain energy from the Bunsen burner *[1 mark]*. This means the iodine particles move more (weakening the bonds between them) *[1 mark]*, and eventually the particles have enough energy to break free from their positions (forming a gas) *[1 mark]*.

c) When the iodine particles are in the gas state, they **collide** *[1 mark]* with the beaker's walls at **high** *[1 mark]* speed. This creates a **pushing** *[1 mark]* force on the walls of the beaker, known as gas pressure.

4 a) i) Observation: e.g. iron can transfer heat, whereas wood can't *[1 mark]*.
Hypothesis: e.g. all metals are thermal conductors and all non-metals are thermal insulators *[1 mark]*.

ii) E.g. the wooden splint will fall from the iron rod within the 10 minutes, but the wooden splint will not fall from the wooden rod *[1 mark]*.

b) E.g. he could burn his hands if he touched the rods *[1 mark]*.

c) E.g. Tim is only looking at a small sample of materials / Tim has not tested all metals and all non-metals *[1 mark]*.

d) Any two from: e.g. most non-metals are dull, whereas most metals are shiny. / Non-metals are brittle, whereas metals are malleable/ductile. / Most non-metals are not hard-wearing, whereas most metals are hard. *[2 marks]*

5 a) As the ethanol and salt are heated, the ethanol evaporates and passes into the condenser (leaving the salt behind) *[1 mark]*. The condenser is a tube surrounded by a jacket of cold water, making the inside of the tube cold *[1 mark]*, so the ethanol condenses when it touches the tube *[1 mark]*. The liquid ethanol then flows down the tube to collect in the beaker *[1 mark]*.

b) 78 °C *[1 mark]*
This is the minimum temperature at which ethanol is a gas and would therefore be able to enter the condenser.

6 a) zinc + hydrochloric acid → zinc chloride + hydrogen *[1 mark]*

b) The mass reading after the experiment would be lower than the mass reading before *[1 mark]*. One of the products is hydrogen, which would escape from the flask, so the mass of the contents of the flask would decrease *[1 mark]*.

c) An acid *[1 mark]*. Zinc oxide is a metal oxide, so it is alkaline and will therefore react with an acid to produce a salt *[1 mark]*.

d) E.g. the melting and boiling points would be different *[1 mark]* as zinc oxide is a compound and compounds have different properties compared to the elements they are made from *[1 mark]*.

7 a) E.g. the greater the number of drops of ammonia, the quicker it diffuses *[1 mark]*. This is shown by, e.g. the litmus paper changing colour 34 s sooner when five drops were used than when one drop was used *[1 mark]*.

b) E.g. the position of the cotton wool/litmus paper within the tube / the temperature *[1 mark]*.

c) The time taken for the litmus paper to change colour would increase *[1 mark]*. In experiment B, the ring of ammonium chloride forms closer to the hydrochloric acid, which shows that the hydrochloric acid hasn't travelled as far as the ammonia in the same amount of time *[1 mark]*. This shows that hydrochloric acid diffuses more slowly than ammonia *[1 mark]*.

8 a) E.g. to stop the metal reacting with oxygen in the air *[1 mark]*.

b) i) magnesium sulfate *[1 mark]*

ii) hydrogen *[1 mark]*

iii) If a lit splint is held near the gas in the syringe, she will hear a squeaky pop *[1 mark]*.

c) i)

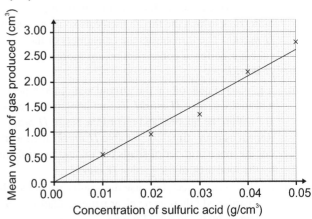

[3 marks — 2 marks for correctly plotting all five data points, otherwise 1 mark for plotting at least three points correctly; 1 mark for a sensible line of best fit]

ii)

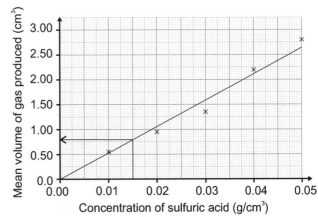

0.80 cm³ (accept between 0.75 cm³ and 0.85 cm³)
[2 marks for correct answer, otherwise 1 mark for showing the working on the graph]

d) i) systematic *[1 mark]*

ii) Subtract 0.1 cm³ from all measurements *[1 mark]*.

9 a) sulfur dioxide *[1 mark]*

b) Because there is less oxygen available higher up in the atmosphere and so some of the kerosene doesn't burn (releasing carbon monoxide) *[1 mark]*.

c) E.g. bubble the gas through a test tube of limewater, which will turn cloudy if the gas is carbon dioxide *[1 mark]*.

Page 138 — Physics Practice Paper

1 a) kg/m³ *[1 mark]*
 b) as the number of components increases, the current decreases *[1 mark]*
 c) refraction *[1 mark]*
 d) Moon *[1 mark]*
 e) conserved *[1 mark]*
 f) the speed of the train is changing *[1 mark]*
 The forces are unbalanced, and the train is moving in one direction along a track, so its speed must change.
 g) buzzer *[1 mark]*

2 a) When it's summer in England the northern half of the Earth is tilted towards the Sun *[1 mark]*, so as the Earth turns, the northern half spends more time in sunlight than the equator *[1 mark]*.
 b) The Earth is positioned between the Sun and the Moon *[1 mark]*.
 c) A solar eclipse is when the Moon passes between the Sun and the Earth, blocking the Sun's light from reaching Earth *[1 mark]*. It is only visible in places on the Earth facing the Sun at the time of the eclipse, so isn't visible across all parts of the Earth *[1 mark]*.

3 a) Advantage: Any one from: e.g. non-renewables produce a lot of energy / non-renewables do not rely on the weather / we don't need to spend money on new technology to use them *[1 mark]*.
 Disadvantage: Any one from: e.g. non-renewables will eventually run out / burning some non-renewables releases carbon dioxide into the atmosphere, which can contribute to climate change/global warming / burning some non-renewables produces sulfur dioxide, which causes acid rain *[1 mark]*.
 b) E.g. there are more hours of daylight in summer than in winter, so more electricity can be generated from solar power / there are generally more clear days during summer so more electricity can be generated from solar power *[1 mark]*.
 c) Energy is transferred from the chemical energy store of the biomass *[1 mark]* to the internal energy store of the water *[1 mark]*.
 d) the Sun *[1 mark]*
 e) It is cloudy so they wouldn't generate much electricity from solar power / the wet climate and fertile soil are ideal for growing plants for biomass *[1 mark]*.

4 a) pressure = force ÷ area = 80 N ÷ 0.5 cm² = 160 N/cm²
 [2 marks for correct answer, otherwise 1 mark for correct equation.]
 b) E.g. make the area of the end of the metal rod smaller *[1 mark]*.
 c) i) 84.1 + 83.6 + 84.4 + 83.9 = 336
 336 ÷ 4 = 84.0 N *[1 mark for correct answer]*
 ii) pressure = force ÷ area
 area = force ÷ pressure
 = 84 N ÷ 140 N/cm²
 = 0.6 cm²
 [2 marks for correct answer, otherwise 1 mark for correct rearrangement.]

5 a) E.g. make sure the ruler is fixed rather than held *[1 mark]*.
 b) To make sure the experiment is a fair test *[1 mark]*.
 c) weight = mass × gravitational field strength
 Rearrange for mass:
 mass = weight ÷ gravitational field strength
 = 1 N ÷ 10 N/kg = 0.1 kg
 [1 mark for the correct formula, 1 mark for the correct rearrangement to show a mass of 0.1 kg.]
 d)

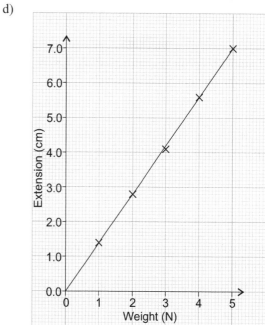

 [1 mark for plotting points correctly, 1 mark for drawing a sensible line of best fit.]
 e) E.g. the extension of the spring increases as the weight suspended from it increases / extension and weight are directly proportional *[1 mark]*. The mean extension doubles from 1.4 cm to 2.8 cm as the weight suspended from it doubles from 1 N to 2 N *[1 mark]*.
 You could have used any of the data given to back up your conclusion.
 f) When Aled repeated the investigation, he got very similar results. This means Aled's results are **precise**. *[1 mark]*

6 a) Current flows through the electromagnet, turning on its magnetic field *[1 mark]*. The sliding bolt is attracted upwards, which locks the door *[1 mark]*.
 b) The weight of the bolt is **smaller** than the force of **attraction** from the electromagnet when the door is locked. *[2 marks — 1 mark for each correct answer.]*
 c) i) 5 cm ÷ 100 = 0.05 m
 speed = distance ÷ time = 0.05 m ÷ 0.05 s = 1 m/s
 [3 marks for correct answer, otherwise 1 mark for correct equation and 1 mark for converting cm into m.]
 ii) E.g. increase the current through the electromagnet / add more turns to the electromagnet's coil *[1 mark]*.
 This will increase the strength of the electromagnet, meaning it will have a stronger force of attraction. This will make the bolt slide (and therefore the door lock) more quickly.

d)

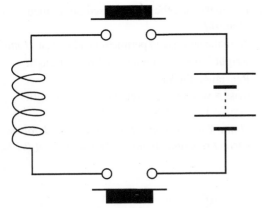

[1 mark for correctly drawn symbols, 1 mark for all the components drawn in series.]

7 a)

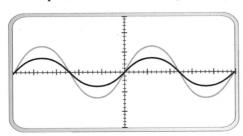

[1 mark for drawing a second wave with lower amplitude and 1 mark for drawing the wave with the same frequency.]

b) Different people have different ranges of frequencies that they can hear/auditory ranges *[1 mark]*, so the sound may have been out of this range for some of the people *[1 mark]*.

c) i) the amplitude of the sound wave *[1 mark]*

ii) E.g. use the signal generator to generate a sound at a chosen frequency, and record the amplitude of the sound as shown on the oscilloscope display *[1 mark]*. Change the frequency of the sound using the signal generator and repeat for many different frequencies *[1 mark]*. Two variables that will have to be controlled each time are e.g. the position of the speaker / the position of the microphone / the volume of the sound from the speaker / the level of background noise *[1 mark for each variable — 2 marks maximum]*.

d) Carry out the investigation again to check that the results are very similar/the same *[1 mark]*.

e) The sound wave would travel more quickly in water than in air *[1 mark]*.

8 a) It aligns itself with the Earth's magnetic field *[1 mark]*.

b)

[1 mark for arrow pointing directly away from North]
The compass aligns itself with the magnet's magnetic field, and the magnetic field lines point from North to South.

c) the size/strength of the magnetic field *[1 mark]*

d) Move each end of the material close to the magnet *[1 mark]*. If either end of the material repels, the material must be a magnet *[1 mark]*.